LEST WE FOR
A tribute to the
and their fam

By
FRED LEIGH.

First published in 1994 by Rose Bank Publications
11, Church Lane, Oulton, Stone, Staffs, ST15 8UL

Printed by Heathland Printers, Strangman Street
Leek, Staffs, ST13 5DU

ISBN 0 9524198 0 7

| Front cover | Parkhouse Colliery |
| Title Page | Holditch Colliery disaster 1937 |

CONTENTS

	Page
Foreword	v
Preface	vi
Acknowledgements and Bibliography.	vii
Glossary	viii
The Explosion at Whitfield.	1
The Lousy Haircut.	6
Talk o' th' Hill Explosion.	13
Yorkshire Bob.	23
Bunkers Hill Explosion.	32
The Elephant Gun and the Pony.	38
Leycett.	51
The Sofa of Genesis.	53
The Explosion at Mossfield of 1889.	58
Into the Depths of Despair.	62
The Strike of 84/85.	68
A Prayer for Christmas.	77
Shaffalong Coalfield.	82
Superstitions.	87
Dust 'Ere.	90
A Visit to the Apedale Small Mines 1993.	92
Ode to Joe.	95
Snappin' Time.	100
Loose It.	104
Miners' Grub Recipes.	108
British Pit Disasters from 1850.	110

FOREWORD

It can be no coincidence that for the second of his tributes to British miners and their communities, author Fred Leigh chooses a title more often associated with the glorious deeds of those who fell in battle than with those who laboured on the battlefield of commerce.

'Lest We Forget' is a phrase to encapsulate the feelings of many who mourn the decline and fall of a once great industry and the countless families who supported it over generations. The sentiment also clearly describes the deep feelings of the author who laments the loss of lives, loss of livelihoods and the disappearance of a way of life.

Fred Leigh has a fine pen for detail and weaves the pathos and despair of colliery disasters, disputes and deprivation with the humour, resilience and closeness of the families who lived in the shadows of the pits.

No-one will fail to be infuriated by the inhumanity of the coal masters who, not content with negligence resulting in the death of miners, then proceeded to turn their widows and children out of tied cottages to make way for replacement labour. But no-one also can fail to laugh at the eccentric characters who populated the pit villages of Staffordshire or be moved by the unexpected gentleness so often shown by the oppressed to the unfortunate.

It is right not to forget; we should be both sad and grateful for the end of an era.

Sean Dooley
Editor
Evening Sentinel
August 1994.

PREFACE.

This book, with the book "Most Valiant of Men" is a tribute to the men who worked in the British Coal fields, and a record of the disasters that occurred.

Let us not forget in years to come what debt we owe to these men and their families in the shaping of our National heritage. Lest we forget the sacrifice, blood sweat and tears, the dangers, hardship, and the struggles for a better wage and conditions that caused so much deprivation and despair.

Remember them with pride.

I have tried also to portray in the several short stories their character, the down to earth humour, the camaraderie and courage probably not known in any other trade and community.

Acknowledgements.

John Abberley, Evening Sentinel
Arnold Cordon
Sean Dooley, Evening Sentinel
Andrew Hopwood, Evening Sentinel
Geoffrey Baker.
Betty Dodd
Vic Dodd.
Clare Kinvig
Keith Meeson.
Roger Simmons.
Ken Stevenson.

Bibliography.

I am indebted to Roger Seifert and John Urwin for passages out of the book "Struggle Without End."

Shaffalong Coalfield from the book "Cheddleton. A village history. " By the Cheddleton Historical and Archaeological Society. First published 1983. 2nd. edition 1994.

Glossary

To help the uninitiated with the North Staffordshire dialect this glossary has been written to translate some of the words used in this book. I may add that the dialect used is not any means a sign of low intelligence or idle speech, on the contrary, it is a part of our heritage, our character, and I hope it will never disappear.

Abite	About	*Afe*	Half
Atner	Aren't	*Ah*	I/ Our
Awee	Away		
Batc	Beat	*Befoer*	Before
Betwain	Between	*Brine*	Brown
Brote	Brought	*Brokken*	Broken
Bin	Been		
Co/Coing	Call/calling	*Cos/Cus*	Cause
Chase	Cheese	*Cosna*	Can't you
Conna	Can't	*Couldst*	Could you
Compo	Compensation		
Dee	Day	*Dine*	Down
Daid	Died	*D'jed*	Dead
Dunner	Don't	*Dust/Dost*	Do you
Eh	He/Aye		
Faither	Father	*Foer*	Four
Foo	Fool	*Fo*	Fall
Fost	First	*Footboers*	Footballers
Funt	Found	*Fer*	For
Gin Giz	Give	*Grind*	Ground
Gooin	Going		
Ite	Out	*Inna*	Is not
Laight	Light	*Lark*	Like
Loose it	End of shift		

viii

Marn	Mine	*Mun*	Must
Munner	Must not	*Mey*	Me
Mower	More	*Mard*	Cry baby
Mac	Make		
Naight	Night	*Noss*	Nurse
Nowt	Nothing	Na	No
Nah	No		
Owd	Old/Hold	*Olwees*	Always
Oss	Horse		
Peen	Pain/Pane	*Pee*	Pay
Pase/Pace	Piece		
Raight	Right	*Rind*	Round
Ser	So	*Stoo*	Stool
Snappin	Meal	*See*	Say
Shape	Sheep	*Sane*	Seen
Shite	Shout		
Thafe	Thief	*Thaivin*	Stealing
Thay/Thee	You	*Tray*	Tree
Towd	Told	*Tack*	Take
Toke	Talk	*Tokin*	Talking
Thase	These	*Theer*	There/They are
Tarme	Time	*Thar*	Your
Taters	Potatoes	*Tharn*	Yours
Ter	To	*Thote*	Thought
Wunner	Wont	*Weshin*	Washing
Weer	Where	*Weet*	Wait
Wom	Home	*Wick*	Week
Woth	Worth	*Waiter*	Water
Wey	We	*Way've*	We have
Yed	Head	*Yo yer*	You

The Explosion at Whitfield Colliery.

Twenty four men and boys were killed, and several injured by an explosion in the Institute pit of the Whitfield Colliery belonging to the Chatterley Iron Company on the 7th. February 1881.

The cause of the disaster was never in doubt. A smithy, situated in the main intake, about 70 yards from the downcast shaft. The hot air and smoke from the smithy was drawn by a flue of 10 inch iron piping for about 15 yards along the level of the main intake and into a side road through a pair of air doors.

It was the opinion of Mr. Wynne, the Senior Inspector of Mines for the area, that it was wrong to place a smithy underground in a fiery mine. In its original position, any heating of the first fifteen yards of the flue was diminished by the cool fresh air in the main in-take near the downcast shaft.

In May 1880 the manager had the smithy moved because it obstructed certain alterations. The effect was that the flue was shortened, and was removed from the cooling current of the main in-take air.

The evening before the explosion was very cold, and the fire in the smithy was lit about 10.30 p.m. by some of the boys. It was disputed whether they were authorised to light the fire. There was evidence that they used coal instead of breeze, consequently making a larger fire, and causing the flue to become red hot.

About 1 a.m. an alarm was given that smoke was spreading into the workings, and on examination, the crosscut where the flue terminated was found to be on fire. As there was no fire hose, efforts were made to fight the fire, using water brought by buckets.

The manager, Mr. Edward Thompson was informed, and accompanied by his two sons and the ex-manager, Mr. Atherton, were soon at the pit head. The manager gave the order to bring up the horses, but no order was given at this time to withdraw the men. By 3 .am. three horses were brought to the surface. Soon the fire was out of control. About 50 men had been fighting the fire, they then tried to save the horses indifferent to the danger to their own lives. Most of these men fortunately came to the surface.

About 3.10 a.m Mr. Edward Thompson and two other men entered the cage, John Thompson the other son was about to set foot in the cage when the explosion occurred. The cage was hurled with great force and became entangled with the pit headgears. John Thompson was caught with a terrible blow on the chin and sent him flying upwards which resulted in a concussion of the brain and his life despaired of. One of the men was thrown out of the cage and fell down the shaft and was never seen again. Edward Thompson and the remaining man managed to retain their hold of the cage and were later extricated with great difficulty from their perilous positions.

The first shock of the explosion was heard many miles away and shook the houses in the vicinity as if there had been an earthquake. The flames burst forth from the pit mouth and set fire to the engine house, and a number of waggons on the bank. At the moment of the explosion the cage in the downcast shaft was being wound up. In the cage they found the water barrel, and in the barrel was the body of Samuel Vickers who had got in the tub to escape the effects of the deadly fire damp.

Despite the weather, which was very cold with a flurry of snow, large crowds began to gather, many relatives of the men and boys still in the mine.

The disaster would have been one of the worst in the country had it happened just a few hours later, when three to four hundred men would have been at work on the day shift.

Mr. Arthur Robert Sawyer, Assistant Inspector of Mines for the district arrived at about 12.30.p.m. Flames and smoke were issuing out of the Laura pit which was the upcast shaft. Sawyer had the debris cleared from around the down cast shaft. The general opinion was that no one could have survived the explosion, but there was one or two men that wanted to go down and see. Before he would allow this he had the water barrel sent down with three torches, for the double purpose of giving anyone who might be alive an opportunity to get into it, and also to

2

ascertain whether the guide ropes were in order. He did this three times, then together with Charles Lowe he got into the barrel and descended. On getting down to 330 yards, they saw the flames and smoke in the pit bottom. They heard no calls or noise of any sort. Thinking it was useless to go any lower they shouted to those above, and were brought to the surface and gave instructions to close the pit.

The flames from the upcast shaft reached 30-40 feet in the air like a giant furnace, a contrast to the weather, for it was snowing hard and bitterly cold. The wooden headgears had gone completely, and lay smouldering on the snow. The engine house was now demolished and the scene was one of desolation. Throngs of people waiting anxiously for news of their loved ones, and some men for news of their workmates.

The Government inspectors, Mr. Wynne and Mr. Sawyer, knowing the intensity of the fire and the explosion, said it was improbable that anyone underground could have survived, and the only possible way to quench the fire was to stifle it. There were present at the scene many mining engineers from various collieries, and they all agreed that the only possibility of choking the fire was to fill it with earth and water. This was achieved by means of diverting a small brook, which ran at some distance from the colliery into the shaft. By means of a plough, and some 30 men digging with shovels a channel made wide enough and deep enough until a good supply of water was obtained.

The inquest commenced on 8th. June 1881, and ended 14th. June, six days of conflicting evidence and 4155 questions and answers. The main topics were the actions of Mr. Thompson the manager, and what he said regarding the saving of the horses instead of the men and the placing of a smithy in the mine.

Coroner to the Jury: *"Gentlemen, you will consider your verdict"*.
The room was cleared at 5 p.m. and the jury returned at 6.20p.m.
Coroner: *"Gentlemen, have you agreed upon your verdict?"*
Foreman: *"Yes"*.
Coroner: *"What is it?"*
Foreman: *"The Jury think the smithy was a mistake and a great error of judgement. Also we find that Mr. Thompson did not take*

sufficient care of the men under his charge, by not withdrawing them from the pit, and not preventing Henry Boulton and Samuel Vickers from descending the pit, he knowing the state of the mine at that time. We find him guilty of culpable negligence, thereby causing the deaths of Samuel Vickers and Henry Boulton. I may say that this is the verdict of 13 out of 14 of the jury."

Coroner: *"It will amount to a verdict of manslaughter."*

Foreman: *"Certainly."*

Coroner: *"The verdict will be that Edward Thompson did feloniously kill and slay Samuel Vickers, and your verdict will be the same as to Henry Boulton."*

List of those killed.

Thomas Hargreaves	37	Dataler
Arthur Holdcroft	25	"
Samuel Gaskell	45	Collier
Richard Cottonbury	30	"
Edward Morton	40	Fireman
William Morton	16	Taker Off
John Sargeant	33	Fireman
George Dale	33	Collier
Joseph Dale	22	"
William Dean	17	Jigger
William Gidman	19	"
Arthur Poole	25	Collier
Samuel Vickers	53	Fireman
John Thompson	26	Ass't Manager Son of Manager
Henry Stubbs	33	Carpenter
Cain Mayer	40	Engineer
Robert Miles	60	Fireman
William Lockett	38	Underlooker
Henry Boulton	29	Fireman
Christopher Beech	49	Lampman
Joseph Beech	22	Dataler

4

John Bailey	42	Dataler
John Davies	46	"
James Fletcher	34	"

On the following Tuesday, a public meeting was held in the Town Hall, Tunstall, with the object of organising relief for the 18 widows and 56 dependent children. The Rev. T.H.B. Fearon, rector of Norton, in which the parish the colliery was situated, explained the urgency of the case which led him to take the initiative in convening the proceedings. He represented the impecunious position of the mining population in consequence of the low wages, and said that in many cases found it impossible to make both ends meet, always hoping for the return of good times to make all straight again. Many of the widows through this explosion had their future perplexed and saddled with debt. In some cases he knew of, the earnings of the men had been so low that they were unable to pay their requisite subscription to their society so as to keep them in benefit.

The directors of the company repudiated any claim for compensation under the the Employer's Liability Act on any grounds of mismanagement. The Chairman of the company in his magnanimity, felt that as there was no legal obligation upon them, there was a strong moral obligation. He therefore had been instructed to say by the directors, that the company would contribute the sum of £250 for the relief fund, and he personally would contribute £50.

Surely the evidence of the enquiry showed without doubt that there had been serious mismanagement. The siting of a smithy in a fiery mine. The failure of the manager to withdraw all his men of which he had plenty of time so to do. The manager was found guilty by a jury of manslaughter. Was not this enough to make the company compensate the dependants for the loss of their loved ones and providers instead of being left destitute?

The Lousy Hair Cut.

Charlie Small entered the living room. He was a sturdy built lad of eleven of average height. His clothes, mostly 'hand me downs' from his elder brothers'. His stockings never fully clad his legs, but reposed at the top of his boots. The leather around the toes of the boots were scuffed, the soles and heels had been repaired many times by his father. His jacket, old and worn, half hid the jersey which bore a large hole in the vicinity of his chest. No tie adorned the collar of his shirt which was crumpled and lay open. A snake buckle belt attempted to hold up his voluminous trousers which reached just below his knees.

"*Mam*" he said holding out a piece of crumpled paper and handing it to his mother who was kneeling on the floor black leading the grate. She half turned and took it from him. Her face was covered in sweat, and somehow, some of the black lead had made streaks on her face. Wisps of her hair had escaped from the bun at the back of her head. This portrait of her gave the impression that she was some demented demon that had escaped from the nether region of Hades.

She slowly laid down the black lead brush on the hearth, and slowly opened the slip of paper. The expression on her face changed from one of devoted labour to one of anger. Her eyes were like lit coals, and she waved the paper under Charlie's nose making him jump backwards.

"*Oo the 'ells given thee this*"? she demanded.
Charlie stepped back in alarm afraid that she was going to strike him.

"*The noss from schoo*'", he answered

"*An' 'ow does she know that yo've got bogies and nits ah'd lark ter know.? eh? The cheek o' some folk it bates may thee anna got anythin' better terdo.*" She was angry now and it showed.

"*Yer con tell 'er from mey this is a clean 'ice this is, an' ah dunner allow them things ter brade in 'ere.*"

Silence ensued for several moments while Charlie's mam rose from a kneeling position, and at the same time tried to move the wisps of hair from her perspiring brow with the back of her hand.

"*It inna only mey.*" Charlie responded prodding himself in the

6

chest with his thumb. *"Thee've o' got 'em in ah class. 'Er says, noss says that thee jump from one yed to another, that's 'ow way've 'o got 'em. "Er was raight upset noss was, and 'er said that the schoo' were infer... infer... wot's it an' got ter bey stamped ite"*.

"*Oh ah, an' does this noss see 'ow?* " Missus Small asked with anger still in her voice, picking up the black lead and brush.

"*Ah*". Replied Charlie sticking his hands in the pockets of his voluminous trousers. *"'Er says, noss says, wey've o' got ter get ah 'air cut short an' gee it a good weshin' wi' carbolic soap"*

"*Oh ah. An' did 'er give thee a tanner ter get it cut?*" She asked making her way to the back kitchen to put away the black leading kit. *"Weer does 'er think ah've got a tanner ter spare on a Thursdee? eh?*

"*Ah dunner know* " Charlie replied, "*Ah'm only tellin' yer wot noss said.*"

Missus Small reappeared in the living room wiping her self on a towel.

"*Raight lad, get a page from thee faither's Sentnel*".
She opened a drawer and took out a stainless steel nit comb and sat down on one of the chairs. She took the paper from him and placed it with care over her knees.

"*Raight me lad, kneel yersel dine 'ere and give us thee yed*".
Charlie did as he was told imagining he was King Charles offering his head to the executioner.

"*Her was raight abite one thing the noss was*".

"*Wot's that mam?* asked Charlie.

"*This mop on thee yed does want cuttin' bad*". She inserted the comb in the mass of thick hair and drew it towards her.

"*Owd on Mam, yer pullin' me scalp ite!*" The protesting muffled voice from Charlie.

"*Owd thee still lad an' dunna bey ser mard. It's fer thee own good*"
More moans from Charlie as the comb traversed his head. She looked down on the paper and sure enough there they were, about a dozen lice. With ruthless determination she immediately set about wholesale slaugh-

Imagining he was King Charles offering his head to the executioner.

ter by squeezing them between her thumb nails.

" *'er was raight abite another thing as well the noss was"*. She managed to say with some effort because her tongue, due to the concentration, was sticking out of her mouth.

"Wots that Mam? The muffled voice of Charlie asked.

"They't lousy lad. It's as the noss said they't infer... wot's it. Ee lad wey anna got tarme ter kill 'em one at a tarme, shift the sel' a minute while ah put thase inter th' fire".

Charlie moved to allow his mother to get up and empty what was left and put them in the fire. She returned to her seat placing the paper again on her knees.

"Give us thee yed again lad an' lets get a few mower." The

process of trawling for lice continued for fifteen minutes or more with the occasional cremation ceremonies.

The door opened and Bill walked in. Bill was an elder brother who a few weeks before had returned from India after serving with the North Staffordshire Regiment as a soldier, and was now working as a collier down Hanley Deep Pit.

"Wot's up wi' the lad"? He asked a bit surprised at seeing Charlie kneeling before his mother with his head in her lap.

"Eh's infer... wot's it wi' lice an' ah'm nit combin' 'im. Noss at schoo' said wey've got ter rid of 'em an' get 'is 'air cut." She answered still intent on the job at hand. Bill walked over to them and looked down at the paper on his mother's lap.

"Crikey!" He exclaimed. *"E is infected an' 'o."*

"That's nowt ah must o' killed 'hundreds o' the little buggers'. It's a wonder ter mey eh's got any yed left".

"Bey quick mam", muttered Charlie, *"Ah've 'ad enough"*.

"Wot 'eh wants, is a good scalpin'" said Bill philosophically.

" 'ave yer got a pair o' scissors ?".

"Ah. Wey?" Missus Small asked.

"Ter cut his 'air wi'. Ah've done a bit in th' army".

Charlie lifted his head and looked at his brother with suspicion on his face.

"Well if yer con, it'll save mey a tanner", said Missus Small getting up and discharging the paper with its load of lice into the fire. She watched and listened intently as the fire consumed them giving off hisses and crackling. The look on her face was one of sheer joy of a job well done.

"W'eer ah thee then?" Asked Bill.

"Wot?" She asked, interrupted from her reverie.

"The scissors".

"Oh ah. Thee'r 'ere in th' table drawer." She answered moving and opening the table drawer. *"Thee anna very sharp mind. Ah've 'ad 'em a long time. Done a lot o' work thase 'ave. Ah thee've bin a good pair thase 'ave. Of even opened tins wi' 'em"*.

Bill took them and examined the blades and smiled.

"It looks lark it. Come on young un let's 'ave thee yed o'er

9

'ere.''

Charlie got up from his knees and walked slowly to the chair that Bill was standing by.

"Sit thee dine lad an ah'll gi' thee a soldiers' trim. Smart an' clean''.

Charlie sat down his jaw firm and set, giving his brother one of his renowned scathing looks.

"At sure yer've cut 'air befoer?''

Bill placed a towel around Charlie's shoulders and taking a comb and the scissors started the first cut.

"Ah've cut more 'air than they'st 'ad 'ot dinners lad, na keep thee sel' still''.

A scream reverberated around the room. It was apparent that poor Charlie was in a lot of pain. Sure enough Bill who was the instigator, was struggling with the clump of hair that refused to be cut without a struggle. He managed after several attempts to cut half the clump, the other half using brute force pulled out. Bill tried again resulting with another scream from Charlie. This went on for another six cuts and Charlie could not endure the torture no longer. The tears that welled in his eyes began to flood and he started to cry. Bill, with all the exertion had started to sweat and was getting irate.

"Wot's up wi' thee yer little mardy, cos na stand a bit o' pain? Ah thote yo' were a tough little bugger, grit thee tathe lad ah shanna bey long.''

By this time Missus Small was getting alarmed at being a witness at her youngest son's torture, intervened.

"Wot doin' at the lad?'' She demanded and inspected the operation. *"My God! Wot a Mess!''* She exclaimed lifting her hands to her face.

"Well what d'yer expect wi' a tool lark thase''. Bill answered with anger in his voice and holding up the offending scissors and mopping his brow. *"Thee wunner cut butter!''-*

Poor Charlie's head looked like a battle field. Eight reasonably sized clumps of hair had been removed from the right side of the skull down to the skin. Poor Charlie was now crying pitifully.

"Wot are yer gooin' ter do na, yer conna carry on lark this"
Bill pondered awhile scratching his own head.
"Get us a basin and ah'll get me razor".
He produced a cut throat razor out of the top drawer of the chest of drawers, and Missus Small produced a basin from the cupboard. The sight of the razor resulted in further anguish from Charlie.
"Wot at gooin' ter do wi' that razor?" He implored.
"Ah'm just gooin ter tidy thee up lad. Just gooin ter tidy thee up. Stick the basin on top of 'is yed Mam.
Missus Small did as she was told with a look of amazement on her face. Bill then proceeded to pare more clumps of hair resulting with more protests from Charlie. This went on for about ten minutes and by this time Bill was losing his temper and Charlie was whimpering and imploring his brother to stop.
"That's enough!" His mother demanded, *"Leave the lad bey. Eh's had enough fer one dee"*. She removed the basin from Charlie's head and surveyed, with a critical eye, Bill's handiwork.
"Wot a mess lad!" She exclaimed. Charlie's whimpering grew louder with the knowledge that is crowning glory had been mutilated, and all the pain he had endured had been in vain.
"Wot d'yer expect wi' tools lark thase" Shouted an irate Bill.
"Tut tut, well ah dunner know, but the lad conner go ter schoo' in this state. Eh'll bey a laughin' stock". His mother expounded.
Silence ensued for several moments except for the occasional sniff from Charlie, and a tut tut from Missus Small.
Then Bill, calmer now, and moved no doubt by pity for his younger brother's predicament, removed the towel from Charlie's shoulders and putting his hand in his pocket extracted a sixpence.
"'Ere thee at lad 'eres a tanner. Put thee cap on an' goo up Tummy Jones the barbers up 'Ope strate. If 'eh says ite, tell 'im it's ma fault. Tell 'im an 'o ter tak it 'o off but leave thee a fringe on the front of thee yed."
Charlie rose from the seat his face streaked with tears caught his reflection in the mirror over the mantelpiece, he half turned to make an askance view

of the back of his head.

"*Crikey!*" He exclaimed "*Wot a mess*"! "*Yo' said yo' could cut 'air yo' did, just luk at it, and 'o that pain ah've bin through*". He looked his elder brother in the eyes with an angry scowl on his face.

"*Well young un*". Bill said apologetically "*Ah've given thee a tanner ter goo an' get it finished off raight, wot more con ah do?*"

"*Ah think ah should 'ave some compo fer the damage an' peen thee'st caused. That's wot ah think dunner yo'Mam*"?
Jack and his Mother looked at each other in surprise then burst out laughing.

"*Yer a cheeky little monkey young un*" replied Bill and reaching in his pocket pulled out a penny. "*'Ere thee at get a penn'orth a rock. Will that compensate thee?*

"*Ah serpose so, ta.*" He put on his cap smiled at his mother and left.

Talk o' th' Hill.

On Thursday 13th. December 1866, an explosion occurred at the Talk o' th' Hill colliery, Talke. Ninety-one men and boys perished. There were two shafts some 300 yards deep. No. 1 pit "Banbury", No. 2 pit "10 feet seams".

One hundred and eighty men descended that day and at 11.15 a.m. there was an explosion. The noise was heard some distance away on the surface. Smoke and debris were hurled with terrific force up the No.1 shaft, such was the force that the cage became detached from the winding rope, and fell down the shaft. Men women and children ran from the village to the pit head anxious about their relatives. Mr. Johnson was the manager and he soon rallied men to serve as the rescue team. The On Setter at the bottom of the shaft was hardly recognisable, such was the extent of his injuries.

Mr. Wynne the Inspector of mines descended the pit in the afternoon. He found the atmosphere terrible and very dangerous, and about 8p.m. he ordered all the naked lights and fires on the pit head to be extinguished and only the miners' safety lamps to be used, such was the dangerous atmosphere even there.

In the cabins close by, men were awaiting their turn to return and assist in the rescue. They were talking of their experiences in sombre voices, how they had seen Bill Stanley in such a place and eight more lying in a ruck, the leg of a man found forty or so yards from the body. A small boy hanging on the neck of his pony.

At intervals the cage in the Upcast shaft brought up more bodies some dreadfully mutilated, the blackened corpses with arms rigid and outstretched, most were half naked, their clothes having been burnt off them. The bodies were removed from the cage and scrutinised in the light of the safety lamps to be identified. The work continued all through the night, and by Friday morning, 58 bodies had been recovered and removed to the Swan Inn at Talke. The "Swan" was to become known as 'The Chamber of Horrors'.

Two rooms at the inn had been provided for the reception of the bodies and identification by the relatives. The mutilated corpses were divested of all clothing or all that was left of it. The scenes were horrendous as mothers, wives and sweethearts bravely did the task of looking for their dear ones. Tears and cries of anguish prevailing for what seemed an eternity.

"Poor George" said one sadly, looking at the remains of George Taylor, *"You have soon followed your wife"* She had died only two weeks earlier.

Turning down the cover of one body, a relative recoiled in horror because half the skull had been blown away.

The cause of the explosion was not known, but several home made keys to the safety lamps were later found in the pockets of the victims.

List of those killed.

E.Denby, J.Grindley, S.Harrison, E.Smith, M.Sherratt, G.Evans. W.Robinson, D.Ball, G.Heath, J.Bosson(13), W.Booth, J.Breeze(13), J.Boughey. L.Cartwright. W.Washington. S.Johnson. S.Kenyon. J.Yoxall. S.Cartlidge. W.Stanley. T.Oldfield. G.Oldridge. N.Billington D.Rigby. T.Dutton. C.Dutton (Father and Son). T.Jenkinson. W.Jenkinson. J.Rigby.(15 an orphan) J.Beddows. T.Griffiths. N.Fletcher. W.Fletcher.(Father and son). W.Ratcliffe. T.Knowles. J.Johnson. P.Twist. J.Booth. J.Yoxhall. J.Sproston. H.Denby. S.Benton. S.Slater. J.Vernon. T.Berrisford. D.Higginson. G.Kent.(19). M.Fletcher. A.Henshall. J.Browning. T.Blackhurst. T.Daniells. D.Colclough. G.Reeves. J.Hart. E.Clowes(14). F.Bailey. G.Boughey.(14). W.Trot. H.Critchlow.(14). W.Archer. J.Madden. - Spencer. E.Cumberland. J.Thompson. T.Smith.(14). N.Taylor. E.Smith.(14). J.Moulton. F.Bereton. J.Macbeth. J.Thompson. D.Cooper. A.Turnock. T.Kent. - Cotton. J.Murray. S.Liptrop. D.Higgins. F.Bailey. G.Reaves. G.Taylor. J.Beddis. J.Whitney.

The Swan Inn. Talke as it is today.

Two rooms had been provided for the reception of the bodies and identification by the relatives. The Inn was known locally as the "Chamber of Horrors".

Top of the shaft, and

cage for decending

17

The Talke colliery

18

where the explosion happened

19

A commemorative window in the church
given by the members of the church in
memory of the mining industry (A. Leigh)

A commemorative plaque to the memory of
George Johnson. Manager of the colliery
at the time of the explosion. (A. Leigh)

20

Just 3 of the many graves of the victims of the explosion that rest in peace in the church yard of St. Martin's Talke

(A. Leigh)

St. Martin's Church Talke. The window, second from the right depicts the awesome scene of the explosion by flames of fire (A. Leigh)

Yorkshire Bob.

Among the hundreds of men who make up the workforce of a colliery, there are always some who by reason of an odd personality quirk or other eccentricity, stand out from the more ordinary individual. Those who conform to what is regarded as normal behaviour usually accept them with amused tolerance.

One of these characters was Robert Dobson, known as Yorkshire Bob, a big rawboned, seafaring, Yorkshireman from Leeds. He came into mining after serving in the Royal Navy in the war of 1939-45. He was demobbed in 1946 and arrived in North Staffordshire to work at the Norton Colliery. He became a legendary figure because of his unconventional life style and his odd personality. Many ex Norton Colliery men will remember Bob and most will have some story to tell about him.

A tremendously strong and muscular man in his youth, he had many facets in his personality. He would be full of the "Joie de vivre" one day and depressed the next. These moods mainly depended on his finances, which like Mr. Micawber forever in the red and waiting for something to turn up. Much of this financial state was caused by his liking for drink, and his poor attendance at work. One being the cause of the other.

After living for sometime in the Miners' Hostel at Bradeley, and presumably to economise on his outgoings, Bob took up residence in a hut on an allotment. This suited him very well, because he only had to pay a peppercorn rent to his landlord. The landlord happened to be the local council, who no doubt would have had him evicted had they known he had taken up residence there. Never the less he remained as a sitting tenant for over twenty years.

However well he ate at his humble abode, he never took any food to work, probably regarding this as another economy. Often he would be visibly watering at the mouth as his workmates ate their food during the short snapping breaks. Pride prevented him from asking for a hand out, but the more soft hearted among his workmates, would offer him a sandwich, a piece of cake or similar which he would accept and devour ravenously. Sometimes the men would give him food of doubtful origin or quality but even this did not deter him. One of the men working on "Five's Bullhurst" face, finished the shift early and not requiring his snappin', placed it behind a roof support in the face return heading. About a week later as Bob sat watching the men eating their snappin', the man who had secreted his unwanted food told him that he had put the food there only the day before. Bob moved quickly and soon retrieved the now stale food from the cache. The bread by this time was now rock hard and the cheese ready to walk away on its own. With great relish he ate every crumb, and it seemed with no apparent ill affect. Such was Bob's digestive system that the next episode may appear to be some-what apocryphal.

One night returning to his hut after a good night out at the pub', a bit bemused by the demon drink, and feeling hungry, he did not light his only means of illumination, a Tilley lamp. He opened a tin which he believed was stewed steak before he retired to bed. The next morning he discovered that the tin of stewed steak was in fact a tin of well-known dog food intended for his Alsation dog, Rex.

"It tasted a treat tha knows", he remarked to his astounded work mate who had a vision of him going on a regular diet of Pedigree Chum, especially after Bob had told him that he had read it in an advertisement in a magazine that the company who produced it claimed that it was good enough for human consumption.

On another occasion he had nothing to eat for over twenty four hours, the reason was that he had no money to buy anything and was eagerly waiting for pay day. After receiving his wages, he went into the nearest fish and chip shop, and ordered three fish and three portions of chips which he liberally dowsed in salt and vinegar. Once out in the street, ate the lot avidly.

"Ah were that 'ungry" he said, *"ah nearly ate th' newspaper thee were wrapped in"*. But wisely he thought that the Sentinel's news print would not have made a satisfactory sweet course.

Although Bob's physical appearance and demeanour looked intimidating, he did in fact have many unexpected sides to his complex nature. He was an interesting conversationalist who could debate on

24

many subjects. He was also an excellent chess and draughts player, taking the logical course in almost anything except his personal life and was probably his own worst enemy

The most appealing side of his nature was his dry and ironic sense of humour. One day, together with a group of miners' making their way inbye to the face in the Bullhurst seam, an electrician working in a sub-station, noticed that Bob was limping from an injury he had sustained the previous day.

"Wot's bin doin' youth"? Enquired the electrician, *"Did'st fo' o'er a bar stoo'"*?

Bob turned to the electrician his face impassive

"Naw" he replied. *"It were like this. Ah tripped o'er one of me set o' Chippendale chairs an' accidently knocked t' Ming Dynasty vase off t' Sheraton sideboard on t'Persian carpet. Pile o' carpet were that thick, ah put me bare foot on one t' broken pieces o' t' vase."*

All of the men including the electrician knew of Bob's domestic arrangements, laughed hilariously.

Bob once aspired to a more genteel social life, and to this end, he decided to take up ballroom dancing. He enrolled at a well known school of dancing in Newcastle-under-Lyme. Bob at that time was working with Vic Dodd, and every week the day after Bob had been to a lesson, he would tell him about his progress. One day they were walking along the main intake level of "Seven's Ten feet", Bob told him that the previous nights lesson had included instructions of how to dance the Fox Trot. Vic knew of Bob's lumbering awkwardness, and he found it hard to visualise him performing such a graceful dance so he persuaded him to give him a practical demonstration. He placed his water bottle at the side of the roadway, and looking in both directions to make sure no one was watching.

"I dont want those daft buggers laughing at me", he said, *"This is what thee call the 'feather step' "*.

In the light of their caplamps, holding his arms high as if holding an imaginary partner, he began a ponderous movement inbye.

"Slow, slow, quick quick, slow ", he intoned while Vic watched

fascinated at this large cumbersome figure. Then it happened! Bob was well known for being accident prone. On the next "Quick", one of his size 12 boots slipped on the highly polished rails in the road haulage track and he executed an unrehearsed double spin and fell between the roof girder middle sets, amid a shower of stonedust and curses. His dance teacher may have been critical of Bob's technique but there was no doubt that his powers of expression in other directions could be most lucid and impressive.

Like most of his forays into forms of entertainment other than drinking, these soon foundered on the rocks of his financial instability. It was only on rare occasions that Bob had full five days pay which he called '*A Noble Five*', at other times he only worked what he described as a '*Desperate One*', being absent from work until Friday. One young miner learning that in one particular week that Bob was being paid one of his rare and famous '*Noble Fives*', congratulated him on his achievement and asked in amazement if it was true.

"*Oh aye*", replied Bob looking askance at the questioner,
"*But it's heavily mortgaged thee knaws*".

Indeed, sometimes, Bob was so financially embarrassed, he would resort to desperate measures in order to rectify his predicament. Sitting in his humble abode one day and with not a penny to his name, he suddenly thought about the empty milk bottles he had never bothered to return to the local corner shop. At that time a penny deposit was charged for the bottle which the shopkeeper would repay on its return. He had over several weeks, dumped about sixty bottles at the rear of his hut, and these were in a very dirty state. He realised that they would have to be cleaned before he could reclaim his deposit, he spent a labourious two hours cleaning them.

"*By th' tarme ah 'ad finished, ah were sufferin' from a cocktail shaker's elbow*", he complained with a wry smile.

His reward for all his effort was five shillings. (25p).

His workmates tried to impress upon him the virtues of working regularly and putting to one side money as a nest egg that could be used for emergencies and such like. The pressure they put on him began to bear fruit and remarkably his attendance record improved and his 'Noble Fives' were achieved more frequently, in fact, he even qualified for a couple of week-end shifts as overtime. One of his close friends at work asked him if he was saving any money.

Bob looked about him furtively, *"Ah, I am"* he replied, *"But not in a Bank or th' post office. Ah dunna trust 'em, thar knowst.*
Ah put me money weer ah can lay me 'ands on it when ah wants it, thar knowst".

"So where do you put it"? His mate asked.
"Ah've constructed a safe down the allotment near to me 'ut.
Ah've dug a hole three feet deep and lined this wi' bricks
At th' bottom of th' 'ole ah've put a large tin box wi' a 'ole in th' lid and in this ah've put a 1½" steel pipe which protudes just above th' ground.
Ah've then covered the chamber wi' 4" thick re-inforced concrete and top o' that Ah've scattered soil".

"Sounds very good ", said his mate *"But how d'yer put the money in?"*
"Easy, ah put Florins (10p) and Half crowns (12½p) down the pipe".
Bob replied, *"It's as safe as Fort Knox that is, nobody'll get in theer in a 'hurry, ah'll tell thee, even if thee find weer it is".*

Predictably, Bob's good intentions did not last very long.

Sitting at home one Saturday night, with very little cash in his pocket and the bright lights of the nearest local beckoning, demons started a ring a ring a roses in his head, he started to moan then the moan changed to a song, a song he had heard long ago: -The Collier's Dying Child.

> *I feel no pain dear mother now*
> *But oh, I am so dry!*
> *O take me to a brewery*
> *And leave me there to die.*

He could stand it no longer, with a cry he seized a seven pound hammer and went out into the night. There was a full moon casting dark shadows in the allotments. He located the cache, the safe he had so carefully constructed. It took him over an hour of frenzied hard labour before he was able to reach his hoard of coins which totalled just over £22. There followed a few days of drinking until all his hard earned money was spent.

'Ah were silhouetted agenst th'full moon'

On his return to work he related to his mate the saga of the break in. *"It were just like breakin' in Tutankhamens tomb."* he said, *Con'st tha imagine th' scene? Ah were silhouetted agenst t' full moon flailin' that 'ammer like a bloody maniac. Ah must've looked summat like Burke and Hare!"*

Some years later, Bob's domicile was shattered. It happened on a monday morning and Bob was taking advantage of one of his days off work and recuperating from over indulgence of drink on the previous night. Suddenly, without warning, there was a terrific crash, a groaning of timber and all the world seemed to be moving. Bob opened his bleary eyes in amazement, was he, he thought, in the first stages of delirium tremens the DTs. The noise of a large machine on the outside started again and the hut began to disintegrate. The old wardrobe reeled drunkenly then fell across his bed. The realisation that this thing that was happening was not in his head brought him to his senses and he started to yell. He could not move now because of the wardrobe that was pinning him to the bed. The noise continued and the roof crashed down and no doubt he would have been seriously injured if not killed if not for the wardrobe. There was a moment of respite, and he shouted for all his worth. The machine outside went silent and he heard voices.

"Ah tell thee I heard some bugger yellin'", said one.

"They't 'earin' things they at", said another.

"Ah tell thee ah 'eard some bugger yellin'".

"The trouble wi' they youth is that thee ast to much sauce last naight and......"

He was interrupted by a strange noise from beneath the pile of wood that had once been Bob's home.

"Help! Help!" The noise seem to be saying.

"Ah towd thee dinna ah 'eard some bugger yellin'."

It took about five minutes to get to Bob who was still in bed with the wardrobe acting as a shield on top of him.

"Wot the 'ell at they doin' 'ere? The amazed demolition man asked.

"Ah was about ter ask yo' the same question." Shouted Bob. *"An' wot the 'ell d'yer think yer doin' knockin' mar 'ut down, wi' me in it? Yer could ah killed me. Well dunner stand theer lark chips get us ite!"*

It took a good half hour to extricate Bob from all that was left of his humble home, and with the exception of a few scratches he was not injured.

"'Ave yer seen me dog"? He asked.

"Dog, wot Dog"?

"Me dog, Rex, me Alsation, 'e were in theer wi' me"

The demolition man shook is head, *"Na ast they youth?"* He answered turning to the other man, who shook his head in reply.

After a frantic search they found poor Rex who unfortunately was dead, killed by the weight of the debris. Bob was a hard tough man but the sight of his friend moved him to tears.

"Some bugger 'll have ter pee fer this"! He cried.

The demolition men expressed their sorrow for the death of Rex and also for Bob's predicament.

"Wey did'na know anybody were livin' in theer, wey were towd by the council ter bulldoze every thin' on thase allotments, because thee want the land ter build on".

Just then a man dressed in a pin striped suit arrived carrying a brief case and a pile of paper under his arm.

"What may I ask is going on here?" He asked.

"An who are yo'?" Bob asked in reply.

"I'm from the council", the man said.

"Yoer just the bugger ah want ter say", shouted Bob angrily,

"D'yer realize that yer've nearly 'ad mar death on yer 'ands, ah were in me bed minding me own business an thase pair, come and knock me hut dine o'er me yed"

"In bed, what here?" Asked the amazed man from the council.

"Aye, 'ere in me 'ut weer ahve lived fer nigh on twenty 'ear".

"But, but you had no right to be living here. Who gave you permission?"

"Ah did na think ah wanted permission," replied Bob *"Any road up ah want compensation fer me dog an me bits an' pieces, and yer'll find me some weer else ter live or else".*

Bob never did get any compensation, on the contrary, the council took a very dim view of him taking up residence on the allotment and were in two minds to charge him for unpaid rates, nor to find him alternative accommodation.

He was however, as a temporary measure, found an haven in the workhouse at Chell and later a house. Living like a normal person did not change Bob at all. He missed above all, Rex his Alsation dog, and he eventually procured another, this time the exact opposite, a Mexican Chihuahua which fitted quite comfortably in Bob's jacket pocket when the occasion demanded. To see this tiny creature trotting at the heels of such a big man was a sight to behold, but he lavished love and care on his little friend that he was rarely seen without it. So much so that he took Pepe', that was his pets name, to the colliery annual dinner dance.

He was aware that the organisers of the dance would not appreciate the dogs presence, so he transported it in a plastic shopping bag hoping that it would not be seen. As the evening progressed however, Bob over indulged and forgot his responsibility, and some of his workmates, knowing about the little dog in the plastic bag, who by this time was getting a little bored and perhaps pining for his master, tried many times to escape. This caused a lot of amusement to people at the surrounding tables. One couple were kept busy frantically pushing the dog back into the bag.

One of the consolations in an occupation like mining is the comradeship of the other miners'. Another is the sense of humour that these men possess. This humour, very often black and down to earth, is an antidote to the hard and dangerous conditions underground. Characters like Yorkshire Bob provided much of this humour consciously or unconsciously, but without any cruel intent. Unfortunately Bob is no longer with us, he will always be remembered by many who worked at Norton with great affection.

Bunkers Hill.

On Friday the 30th April 1875, 42 men and boys were ushered into eternity, and another died of his injuries later. Twenty two women and 56 children were left without husbands and fathers. The explosion occurred about 1 p.m. in the "8 foot" seam and all working there perished. The rescue teams had great difficulty pushing forward the rescue task. The melancholy task of picking up the bodies, was lying heavily on their minds. By 9 p.m. they had recovered 12 dead bodies. The dead were found in groups of three and four and appeared to have been running away from the apprehended danger. Some were sitting down, others had their hands in front of their eyes as though trying to ward off some approaching ill.

By 5 a.m. on Saturday, 42 bodies had been brought to the surface, and it was assumed that it was the full total to be recovered. All the bodies were taken to the Swan Inn at Talke for identification. The same Inn was used for the same purpose in 1866 for the Talk o' th' Hill Colliery disaster in which 91 men and boys were killed.

There was a morbid scene when Joseph Ashmore could not find his son, having had to re-examine the remains again and again. He was adamant that his son was not there. The rescue team descended the pit again. After an intensive search they found Joseph Ashmore's body at the far end of the workings.

Daniel Charlesworth aged 13 was still alive when he was brought to the surface, but died shortly afterwards.

The bodies had been washed and placed on boards in rows - a pitiful sight. Identification was very difficult in some cases for the disfigurement was awful. W. Moore a fireman, his face was unrecognisable, and could only be identified by his curly hair.

The Inquest.

The only witness was William Stevenson who had been called to identify his son, James. He was at work in another seam, and he said that he heard a noise and thought it was a fall of roof. He did not think that an explosion had occurred, even his lamp was not affected.

The cause of the explosion was a mystery. The practice of "blasting" had not been long introduced in the mine. The prior method was by "wedging". It can only be assumed that the explosion was due to shot firing. This could be the reason why fireman Moore's face was so badly disfigured?

List of the Dead.

W. Maxfield. T .Lawton. W. Hancock. E. Hancock, J. Stevenson. (15). J .Beckley. D. Charlesworth. (13). T. Peats. (17). D. Boston. J. Rogers. (16). T. Thompson. (17). T. Beech. D. Fox. J. Nield. E. Burton. (19). J. Boyd. (13). T. Holland. J. Hancock. (18). G. Breeze. S. Morris. G. Holland. J. Chadwick. W. Boughey. (14). H. Dean. T. Dean. (14). J. Holland. L. Ashmore. (13). W. Moore. H. Moore. (13). R. Dale. (13). J. Higgins. R. Jackson. J. Lucas. J. Yearsley. J. Carter. W. Proudlove. (13). J. Marshall. (17). J. Stubbs. (18). T. Mason. J. Ashmore. N. Sumner. E. Baddeley.

In some cases father and son died together.

The two Hollands were brothers'.

Bunkers Hill Colliery

POSTSCRIPT.

The following information was kindly sent to me from a Mr. Colin Yearsley in Denton, Manchester, whose great grandfather, James Yearsley was killed in the disaster. This information about his family gives an insight into the suffering of such families when the father was killed. The deprivation and despair highlights the heartlessness of the mine owners in those days.

James Yearsley was born at Smallwood Cheshire c1848. At the age of 23 married Mary Jepson in 1871. About this time they moved to Butt Lane and he was working at the Bunkers Hill Colliery owned by W. Rigby.

On the 2nd. April 1871 a son was born and named Alfred William. On the 7th, March 1873 a second son, Jacob was born and on the 28th. December 1874 another child, James was born.

A few months after the last child was born, on the 30th. April 1875, an explosion occurred at the Bunkers Hill Colliery and the father lost his life leaving Mary a widow and three small children aged 4 months to 4 years of age to nurture feed and find a home for.

Yes to find a home for. Within weeks after the disaster she was given notice to quit because the little house they lived in, apparently was owned by the colliery, and was needed by another collier and his family.

Can anyone in todays caring society, imagine the anguish that this poor lady experienced. The loss of her dear husband with no money and the final straw to be homeless. A little later on May 15th 1875, now at her wits end, she received a curt note:

Mrs. Mary Yearsley
Bunkers Hill Colliery Accident Relief Fund.
A sum of money has been subscribed for the relief of the sufferers and as long as the money lasts each widow so long as she remains chaste and unmarried, will receive 4 shillings per week, and each child up to the age of 13 years 2 shillings per week.

34

Oh how relieved she must have felt, what a windfall. 10 shillings per week (50p). This money was raised by public subscriptions and the mine owner had the gall to countersign the note. Not even a letter of condolence.

The writer does not know where she went to live after being told to quit her home in Butt Lane, but on the 2nd of December 1880, five years after the disaster, she died at Smallwood. She was just 34 years of age. She was interred in James's grave. The three boys went to live with Mary's mother, and in 1889 the eldest boy, Alfred, went to live in Denton, Manchester, he would now be about 18 years of age. The two other boys, Jacob and James found work on farms in Cheshire, and a letter dated 13th. October 1889 from James the youngest to Alfred asking him to *'Write a bit oftener'*. Tragedy was to strike again for on the 13th. December 1889, James died from diphtheria. The farmer they worked for, not wanting the other son, Jacob, to catch the disease locked him in a barn with a burning sulphur candle. Fortunately he survived, James was 14 and he too was interred with his parents.

'Man's inhumanity to man
Makes countless thousands mourn'.
Robert Burns.

HC 069222

D. Cert.
S.R.

CERTIFIED COPY of an ENTRY OF DEATH
Pursuant to the Births and Deaths Registration Act 1953

Registration District **Newcastle-under-Lyme**

1875. Death in the Sub-district of **Audley** in the **County of Stafford**

No.	When and where died	Name and surname	Sex	Age	Occupation	Cause of death	Signature, description, and residence of informant	When registered	Signature of registrar
Columns:—	1	2	3	4	5	6	7	8	9
23	30th April 1875 Bunker's Hill Colliery	James Yeareley	Male	27 years	Collier	By Explosion of Fire Damp "Accidental Death"	Certificate received from John Booth Coroner for Staffordshire Inquest held 1st May 1875	Twentieth May 1875	George Proctor Registrar.

Certified to be a true copy of an entry in a register in my custody.

....

.... Superintendent Registrar.

10th August, 1987 .... Date.

CAUTION:— Any person who (1) falsifies any of the particulars on this certificate, or (2) uses a falsified certificate as true, knowing it to be false, is liable to prosecution.

36

Mrs. Mary Yearsley

Bunker's Hill Colliery Accident Relief Fund

A sum of money has been subscribed
for the relief of the sufferers and as long
as the money lasts each widow & so
long as she remains chaste and unmarried will
receive 4/- per week, & each child up
to the age of 13 years 2/- per week.

May 1st 1875.

W. Wm Hutchin -

Wm Rigby

The Elephant Gun and the Pony.

Church over for the day, errands and other duties done, Charlie sallied forth to see what the gang were up to. He found them at the corner of the street. They were all there, Eric Smith, Jackie Chawner, Arthur (Ginger) Williams, Georgie(Gudder) Mountford.

They all watched in amazement, Ginger Williams marching up and down with a large rifle on his shoulder pretending no doubt to be a soldier.

"Wot's got theer?" asked Charlie equally amazed.

"Eh says, Ginger says it's an elephant gun". Replied Gudder.

"A wot"? Charlie asked.

"An elephant gun. Wot yer shoots elephants with"

"Thee wants an elephant gun"! Exclaimed Charlie. *"'Ow dust thay know"?*

Ginger swung the gun around pointing the barrels at Charlie.

"That's easy. Just luk at them 'oles, the 'er big'ns anna thee? So the bullets ah big anner thee?. An' the've got ter bey big bullets ter kill elephants, anner thee? Any foo' knows that."

The words of wisdom irritated Charlie who didn't like to be enlightened by one of his subordinates. He grasped the gun with both hands and after few moments wrestling relieved Ginger of his prize possession.

"At they co'in' mey a foo'?" Asked the now irate Charlie.

"Ah did'na see they was't a foo'. Any road giz me gun back it's marn", Ginger pleaded.

Charlie raised the shot gun to his shoulder and with some difficulty aimed it at the ever rebellious Ginger, and pulled the trigger. "BANG!" He exclaimed. *"They't d'jed ah've blown thee yed off"*. He started to laugh and the others laughed too. He lowered the gun and started to examine it.

"It's o'raight this is it'll come in 'andy wen wey plee cowboys an' injuns wunner it?. We' dist get it from any road?"

"From a kid in ah class at schoo'. They knowst Billy 'iggins. Ah swopped 'im ma set o' fag cards of footboers', two 'Otspurs, thray

38

wizards an' a catapult fer it. 'E said, Billy said, 'is faither 'ad given it to 'im fer 'is birthdee. ''

Charlie reluctantly handed the gun back to Ginger. After all he was fair, and he had said so on many occasions, for he was very proud of the many quotations he had stored in his memory to be spouted when the time was apt. These he had gleaned from his father who was an avid book worm. There were times however, when the words were not exactly has they were written. But never the less, were so many words of wisdom and were listened to by his entourage in awe.

"Render therefore unto "Cee saw" this thing w'ich is "Cee saws''.

He looked at his disciples, a slight superior smile on his face to see if his pearls of wisdom had given the desired effect. It had for they all with the exception of Ginger, stood transfixed with mouths agape.

"Wot on abite? See-saws. This elephant gun belongs ter mey ah 've towd thee, ah swapped it fair an' square. '' Ginger replied defiantly. Charlie was about to remonstrate with him when he espied an alien face looking intently at the gun.

Jimmy Cliffe was a couple of years younger than the rest of the gang, and was rarely seen by them because his parents for some reason, kept him apart. His father was a carter working for himself. He owned a horse and two carts, one four wheel flat which he used to convey crates from the crate yard which was situated at the Grange, to his customers, the potbanks. The other was a dray which was used to cart shards from the potbanks to the marl hole or the shard ruck. The horse was a magnificent animal some seventeen hands high, but not a Shire and was referred to as a cart horse.

"Does thee faither know they't 'ere''? asked Charlie.

Jimmy did not answer for all his attention was absorbed in the shot gun now in a 'Shoulder arms' position on Ginger's shoulder.

"Oose is the gun?'' Jimmy asked, his gaze still coveting the firearm.

"It's marn'', replied a boastful and proud Ginger. *"Wey''?*

"Dost want ter sell it''? Jimmy asked.

"Cus ah dunner''. Retorted Ginger.

Charlie and the rest of the gang remained in silence. Their heads like tennis spectators turning from Ginger to Jimmy in turn.

"Ah'll swop thee some it fer it''. Jimmy said eagerly, is eyes still not leaving the prize he yearned to be his.

Ginger by this time was marching up and down like the soldiers' he had seen at the pictures. Whether Ginger had heard him or not was hard to say, so intent was he acting out his charade.

Jimmy could not stand being ignored a moment longer and he lunged forward on Ginger's next about turn, grasping with both hands the stock and the barrel in an effort to seize the gun.

The onslaught by Jimmy took Ginger by surprise, and he stumbled backwards. The gun was now in Jimmy's hands and a strange weird gleam came into his eyes as he inspected his prize.

"You cheeky little bugger''! Exclaimed a surprised Ginger having gained his equilibrium,he moved forward to remonstrate with the audacious thief and retrieve his property. Jimmy stepped backwards bringing the stock to his hip with one hand on the barrel the other on the trigger.

"Stick 'em up or ah'll put a bullet raight between thee eyes''!

Retorted Jimmy, his face grim and his voice was so earnest that he meant every word he said.

The remark halted Ginger dead in his tracks. For a moment he believed that Jimmy would do what he said, then it dawned on him that the gun wasn't loaded, confirmed also by Charlie's laughter followed by further giggles from the others. This enraged Ginger, and he grasped the barrel and, put a clenched fist against Jimmy's nose in a threatening gesture.

"Ah've a good mind ter put this raight between thar eyes, na give us me gun''

Jimmy still held on, his face still grim.

"Ah've warned thee'' He shouted ignoring Ginger's fist he pulled the trigger. A look of surprise came over his face when nothing happened looking down at the gun he pulled the trigger again.

"Yer little bugger. Did yer sey that Charlie? the little Bugger would a shot mey!'' He looked at Charlie as though to be excused from his next action which was a violent push on Jimmy's head which made the lad stumble backwards and releasing the gun to its rightful owner. Ginger

returned the gun to the 'Shoulder arm' position.

"They cost think thee sel' lucky they cost young un, that ah anna gi' thee a good 'idin'''.

Jimmy picked himself up from the floor is face sullen his bottom lip quivering.

"Yo'd best be gooin wom afer eh changes 'is mind, Ginger con bey very nasty wen eh's a mind''. Charlie advised him.

"Ah only wanted the gun'' Jimmy said now on the verge of tears.

"But thee cos na 'ave it. Con yer?. It's 'is. Nar off yer goo''

"Ah'll give 'im anythin' for it'' Jimmy pleaded. *Ah'll even swop 'im me pony.''*

Ginger stopped dead in his tracks. The others including Charlie looked at Jimmy with mouths agape and eyes standing out like organ stops.

"A pony!'' Exclaimed Charlie. *"A pony. Dost mean a real pony lark thee faither's 'oss but littler?''*

"Ah a real pony, o' brine eh is an' abite this big''. Jimmy answered his confidence returned raised his hand to Charlie's shoulder. *"Ee, Ah''* The gang added all in unison.

"Is it tharn?'' Charlie asked getting excited.

"Cus it's marn. Me faither give it mey fer me birthdee''.

"Wots see ter that Ginger. At gooin' ter swop 'im?''

Ginger rested the stock on the ground and with his free hand started to scratch his mop of red hair vigorously hoping that this may help him to make this momentous decision.

"Well?'' Asked an impatient Charlie, *"Wot gooin' ter do ?''*.

"Ah dunner no''. Ginger replied a worried look on his face.

"Ah'll 'ave ter sey th' pony fost''.

"Ah'' The gang murmured in unison excited now that they would soon see the pony and, may be get a ride.

"We 'er is the pony any road''? Asked Charlie, now taking charge of the situation.

"It's up the Grange we me faither keeps 'is 'oss. Way 've got a stable up theer''.

41

The Grange was a large tract of land of about 400 acres that was part of the Shelton Iron Steel & Coal complex formerly known as Rushton Grange a farm or villa and was in existence and recorded in the great survey of landholding of 1086 in the Doomsday Book. Cistercian monks from Hulton Abbey lived there circa 1235 and on its dissolution, was sold to the Biddulphs.

It was steeped in history, myths and hauntings. A plague came to the Grange carried by the clothes of an Italian governess in the employ of the Bagnall family. The governess died of the plague , and so did several members of the family. The disease spread to their neighbours and were buried in pits near to the Grange.

Jimmy's father stabled his horse and pony in a makeshift corrugated steel and wooden building near to the crate maker's yard from where Jimmy's father transported the finished crates to various potteries, who packed their wares in them to ship them all over the country and the world.

"'eres me faither's stable". Jimmy said on reaching the ramshackle building. *"But the pony wunner bey in 'ere. 'E'll bey grazin' some weer"* He entered the stable and reappeared a few moments later with a rope.

"Wot's that fer?" Asked Charlie pointing to the rope.

"Ter catch 'im with. Ah'll mak' a lasso and throw it o'er is yed". Replied Jimmy making a noose in the end of the rope.

The Gang looked at each other in turn smiling,

"Dost mean like the cowboy's do on th' pictures"? Asked Ginger still carrying his prize possession in the crook of his arm.

"Ah", said Jimmy.

"They! At they seein' they cost lasso a 'oss? Ah dunner belave thee."

"Weet an'see then", said Jimmy coiling the rope and setting off across the field. They followed him, and there silhouetted against the sky line near to the headgears and buildings of the disused Grange pit was the pony grazing.

"Wey'll 'ave ter sneak up on it", whispered Jimmy *"So bey quiet"*.

"Wey is it wild?" Asked Charlie.

"It inna really wild. But it anna bin brokken yet, me faither anna 'ad

tarme''.

"Wot's mean brokken?'' Asked a surprised Ginger.

"Brokken in.'' Whispered Jimmy. *"Eh's gotta be learnt''*

"Wot's mean learnt?'' Ginger asked for this was a new experience for him and of course all the other lads. Ponies and horses were something they had hardly had anything to do with. They saw them pulling the carts in the street and Charlie had heard his older brother who worked in the pit, talk about his 'Blackie' the pit pony he worked with pulling tubs in the pit.

But it never occurred to any of them that the animal like all animals had to be taught to obey commands, and trained for a specific job.

They moved forward stealthily, like hunters tracking their prey.

"Me faither used ter work dine theer.'' Charlie said as they passed the old mine. *"In fact eh was the last bloke ter come ite''.*

"'Ush quiet.'' Admonished Jimmy.

The pony lifted his head and looked around. He saw several small humans approaching him stealthily. He whinnied, turned then started to walk away.

"Ah towd yer ter keep quiet''. Jimmy retorted angrily. *"Eh's gooin' ter tak some catchin' na''.*

"Lasso 'im then, '' replied Ginger.

"Ah conna rope 'im from 'ere. Con ah''?

"Shut thee face Ginger an' bey quiet.'' Charlie ordered and, thinking at the same time it was about time he took command.

"Raight ah think this needs a plan else wey're gooin ter be o' dee''.

"Wot plan?'' Replied the ever rebellious Ginger. *"They'st o'wees got a plan they ast. It inna thar 'oss an' it'll bey marn wen wey catch it.''*

"Ah've towd they ter shut thee face anna ah! There was a strict order of command in Charlie's voice.

"They red yed, cost tak' Eric an' Jackie an' mak thee wee rind the pony on his other side. Dunner let'im sey yer. Then wen ah shite raight, wey'll 'o' move in on 'im''

The three moved off, with Ginger muttering something incoherent. By this time the pony was grazing again unaware that a mind greater than his

43

was planning his capture.

About five minutes had elapsed and, Charlie stood up to espy the deployment of his troops. He saw that they were ready and gave the order. *"Raight move in"*.

The pony, startled by the urgent command, stopped grazing and lifted his head to see the approaching boys on both flanks then shook his head in an arrogant gesture, lowered his head and continued with his meal. The posse approached slowly and with stealth, hardly daring to breath to within about a yard of him. Jimmy slowly prepared the lasso.

"Quiet. Careful" Charlie whispered. The pony raised his head again his eyes meeting Charlie's, and they stared each other out for a few moments as though weighing each other up.

The rope whistled through the air and landed not on his neck as intended but on his back. The pony who did not like things that whistled and landed on his back, showed his displeasure by a whinny and rearing on his hind legs. In that moment in time he could see that he was outflanked and outnumbered but that the way ahead was clear. The General it seemed had not created an impasse in his deployment of troops, and so the pony saw the way to escape was through this bottle neck and he bolted like Pegasus with wings. The boys' mouths were wide with amazement, stupefied by the speed of the ponies bid to escape. The silence that ensued was broken by the angry voice of Ginger:

*"Ah thote yo said yo could lasso 'im like a cowboy. "*Then started to prod the sad looking Jimmy in the stomach with the elephant gun. *"They't a liar they at!"* Jimmy was by this time was near to tears, and the prodding of the gun in the tender part of his anatomy made matters worse.

"Leave the lad bey", said Charlie and removing the barrel of the gun from Jimmy's stomach. *"Eh tried 'is best, any road we'd best concent' wot's it on catchin' the pony and, remember this red yed."* He paused and looked Ginger straight in the eyes.

"A bird in thee 'and is woth two in a bush" The proverb fell on stony ground as far as Ginger was concerned.

"Na wot at thee on abite, wey anna after birds wey're after a 'oss, an' 'im 'ere said eh could lasso it. " Ginger replied and proceeded to prod

thc unfortunate would be cowboy in the stomach again with the gun.

The sun was now high in the sky and a sirocco type breeze made the temperature soar. The landsape of the Grange was now changing and taking on the colour of a Texan cattle range because of weeks without rain. The Gang were now feeling the heat and had taken off their jersey's, and tied them about their waists, the sweat running freely down their freckled faces.

"Ah could just drink a pint o' dandelion and burdock". Muttered Jackie Chawner, wetting his parched lips with his tongue.

"An' mey" said Gudder taking the elastic bands off his stockings and lowering them to his ankles.

"A drink o' waiter would do mey", said Jimmy Steele sauntering away with his hands in his pockets. Then an urgent cry almost like a croak from his parched throat.

"Eh's theer! The ponies theer!"

"Weer?" asked Charlie shielding his eyes from the sun with his hand.

"Theer" Repeated Jimmy Steele pointing. *"Theer 'avin' a drink o' waiter from 'Forty Foot' "*!

'Forty Foot' was a small mere and named after the assumption that in its deeper part, in the centre, that it was forty feet deep. The older generation said that it was bottomless, and had evolved from an old mine shaft and that the crater was made when the shaft had collapsed. No tributary kept the water at a constant level but was fed from the flooded mine workings like an artesian well.

The heat of the day was forgotten now, for the excitement of capture gripped them. Stealthily, they made their way to the waters edge, no orders given and hardly any sound. Young Jimmy Cliffe took charge and indicated with a wave of his hand for the rest to be still. He walked slowly to the pony talking softly. The pony raised his head and appeared to recognise his little man and whinnied softly. Jimmy took the advantage and with care placed the noose around his neck.

"Eh's got 'im." Shouted Charlie with excitement and walked briskly towards Jimmy and his prize followed by an equally excited gang.

"Inner 'e luvely"?.Murmured Gudder.

45

"Ah." Said Eric.

"Eh is", said Jimmy Steele.

"Inner 'e nice?" Said Jackie.

"Ah", replied Charlie, *"A little belter"*.

The pony shivered when he felt five pairs of hands stroking his flanks and back, and started to pull away.

"Whoa", ordered Jimmy tugging hard on the rope, *"Whoa"*.

Ginger stood holding the gun by the barrel appraising the situation.

"Well?" asked Charlie. *They'st said nowt yet. At gooin' ter swop 'im or at ner?"*

"Ah'm thinkin'. Replied Ginger.

"Wot with"? Said Charlie with sarcasm.

"It's o'raight fer they. It inna thar gun. It's a big decis'...wot's it mak. Any road up ah've got ter try it ite. Anna ah?

"Wot's mean, they ride it?" Asked Charlie smiling.

"Ah mey",replied Ginger,sticking his chest out and prodding himself with his thumb. *"It's no good ter mey if ah conna ride it. Is it?"*

"Goo on then, let's sey thee." Urged Charlie.

"Wot? Asked Ginger.

"Ride 'im thick yed".

"'Ere owd this." Ginger said handing the gun to Eric. He moved to the pony and touched him for the first time. *"'Ow do ah get on?"* He asked young Jimmy.

"They'st seen Tom Mix jump on 'is 'oss ast ner at th'pictures?"

"Ah," replied Ginger. *"Lark this"?* He took a few steps backwards, a run and with a leap frog, landed on the pony's back. The pony of course was startled. Never in his young life had the pony ever had anything on his back, but this he knew was one of those daft little men, and he did not like it one little bit so, it had to go and fast. He bolted dragging young Jimmy along with the rope, and Ginger hanging on to his mane as though his very life depended on it. The Gang stood spellbound, mouths agape and eyes standing out like organ stops. After about a hundred yards, the pony halted, the nostrils flared and a wild look in his eyes. Then, he started to buck. Up and down went Ginger still hanging in desperation to the

pony's mane. Young Jimmy, picked himself up from the floor and let go the rope thinking it was prudent to do so. Charlie and his merry men, now recovered from the initial shock, burst into hilarious uncontrollable laughter, to see the dour face of Ginger white as a sheet, his hair seemed to have taken on a more redder hue in contrast.

"Ride 'im cowboy." Shouted Charlie in between the bouts of mirth. Then it happened. Ginger bounced a good foot from the pony's back and he landed as though stunned on his backside on terra firma.

The pony realising he had ridded the foreign body from off its back, took wings and was last seen near the canal in Macalonie about a mile away. A gruff loud voice interrupted the boys revelry and they all turned as one to see from whence it came.

"Wot th''ell are yo lot doin' wi ma pony"? It was young Jimmy's father, the carter Mister Cliffe. *"Ah said wot ah yo lot doin' wi' me pony"?* He then noticed for the first time his son Jimmy, who had just picked himself off the floor.

"An' they, wot ah yo doin' 'ere wi' this lot eh? 'ow many tarmes 'ahve ah towd thee ter keep awee from this lot eh''?

"Thee wanted ter see the pony dad''. Jimmy replied sheepisly.

"Ah'll gi' thee pony wen ah get thee wom''. Mister Cliffe said with anger in his voice. *"An' yo lot bey off wi yer an' leave ma lad alone in future. "*

"Does this mean'', ventured Ginger, holding the gun up. *"That yer anna gooin' ter swop the pony fer me gun?"*

A black cloud seemed to fill the sky at this moment in time. The pink of Mister Cliffe's face changed to a reddish purple.

"Gun!" He exploded. *"Gun, Pony! Ah'll gi' yer pony bey off wi' yer or ah'll tak me strap to yer!"* His hands quickly went to unbuckle his strong wide leather belt.

The Gang without further ado, took to their heels thinking no doubt it was prudent and very wise so to do. They ran until they reached the entrance to the Grange at the little shop on the corner. Breathless, perspiring and looking in the window at the rows of pop bottles, and with envy at the little girl who was being served with a large ice cream. She passed them on the threshold, holding in her hand the large cone of mouth watering ice cream, her tongue like a serpent taking it in her mouth avidly, her eyes as though on a pivot looking at each boy in turn. The gang, their drooling mouths open, and their eyes not leaving the ambrosia, which they yearned to be theirs.

"Giz a lick", the croaking voice of Ginger begged. *"Giz a lick and ah'll let yer 'old me elephant gun"*. The girl held his gaze for a few moments, her tongue still taking in the delight like a temptress. Then she turned and ran away looking behind her as she went.

"Yer skinny wench". The croaking voice shouted after her.

Charlie shook his head and gave Ginger one of his scathing looks, and entered the shop.

"A 'aypenny cornet please." He felt in his pocket withdrew the coin and offered it to the lady on the other side of the counter. She was kind hearted and seeing the perspiring faces watching her, gave Charlie a good measure on the small cornet.

They were all agog as they watched their leader come amongst them. He took a lick, savoured it and watched their faces. He took another then turned to the nearest holding the cornet to his mouth. *"Have a lick"*, he said benevolently. Then to each boy in turn until it was gone. This feeling of benevolence reminded him of the parable he had heard at church that very morning, of Jesus feeding the five thousand with five loaves and two fishes, and he felt some how elated. After all, an halfpenny cornet shared between six sweaty souls was in Charlie's estimation a bit of a miracle.

They entered the street where they lived, tired, hot and sweaty. Quite a few occupants of the houses were out doors. Their chores done, they sat on chairs, stools and the steps, enjoying the late afternoon sun and gossiping. Standing out like a sore thumb amidst this congregation, were two men, one with a mop of red hair, his arms gesticulating as though in anger. The other man, balding and squat. Red hair paused when he spied the boys enter the street.

"Ginger!" He shouted angrily. *"Come thee 'ere"!*

Ginger marched slowly to him followed by the others. A look of apprehension on his normal dour countenance.

Before Ginger could reach him the balding squat man ran forward and snatched the gun from him.

"This is it! This is me gun"! The man exclaimed.

"It inna it's marn!" Shouted Ginger wrestling with the man to claim back his property.

"It inna tharn. It's marn, they'st pinched it from ma lad yer young thafe"!

"Owd on. Owd on". Said the red headed man. *"Ma lad says it's 'is, so let's 'ear wot eh's got ter see fer 'imsel' befer yo con ca'ing him a thafe."*

Ginger's dad was a strong muscular man with a temper that matched his hair, and made worse by being aroused from his slumber, because he was on the night shift at the Sneyd Colliery. He took the gun from the man and stood it up against the wall.

"Raight me lad. Is this gun tharn?"

"Yes Dad", replied Ginger. *"Ah swopped Billy 'Iggins me set o' fag cards o' footboer's, me two 'otspurs, threy Wizards an' me catapult fer it"*.

"An' oose Billy 'iggins?" Asked Ginger's dad.

"'Eh's ma lad." Replied the balding man. *"Eh took it from me cupboard in ah 'ouse, an' 'e said, ma lad said, that yo'er lad pinched it from 'im"*.

"Luk they!" Said Ginger's Dad, taking up the gun and pointing at the man. *"Ma lad inna a thafe. Eh's bin brote up proper eh as, not dragged up. So if thee wants thee gun back, yo bring ma lad's property back. Then yer con 'ave thee gun. O' raight?"*

He was about to disappear into the house with the gun when he turned, *"An' if ah were yo, ah'd gi' that lad a yoer's a beltin' fer thaivin' the gun off they in the fost place."*

The door closed with a bang. The man, a heavy scowl on his face walked briskly along the street.

Charlie looked at his men and started to smile. They all smiled back at him with the exception of Ginger, who it seemed was on the verge of tears. Charlie put his hand on his shoulder.

"Never they mind Ginger, thase one thing thee'll never tak from thee".

"Oh ah. An' wot's that?" Asked Ginger with a querulous look on his face.

"That thee at na a chip off th'owd block." Answered Charlie trying to instill a modicum of humour. But alas, the quotation fell on stony ground. Ginger shook Charlie's hand from his shoulder impatiently, and the look on his face returned to its normal dour look.

"Na wot on abite? Chips! Wot's chips got ter do wi' mi' elephant gun ah'd lark ter know."

Fair Lady Pit, Leycett.

A little after the day shift had started, a terrible explosion occurred, succeeded by a rumbling that could be heard many miles away. The earth literally shook likened to an earthquake. Volumes of smoke and debris vomited violently from the shaft as awesome as a volcano.

Messengers were sent for aid, for medical men and engineers. Volunteer rescue men soon assembled on the bank, and soon this brave, valiant "freight" descended into the abyss. The heat and smoke was unbearable and after a few moments, the rescue team, reluctantly, had to ascend to the surface. There could be little wonder at this retreat. None of these brave men had any breathing apparatus. So eager they were in attempting to rescue their comrades, they preferred not to loose a moment, awaiting upon the arrival of the equipment.

On the 21st day of January 1880. Sixty two, men and boys perished. There had been previous disasters, Leycett had had its share of sacrifices of humanity.

12th. January 1871. 8 killed.
12th. September 1879. 8 killed.
16th. October 1883. 6 killed.

To return to the events of January 21st 1880 the worst of the Leycett disasters:- It was not until noon of the same day that practical help could be given. On entering the workings, the terrible destruction was fully realised. Without delay the few survivors were taken to the pit bottom and then to the surface. Butty, W. Burgess was found with his two sons. The two young men were dead but the father was still alive. The poor man was terribly injured, the flesh literally hanging from his body. He walked bravely unaided, to the 'Hovel', the place set aside for receiving the dead and the injured.

The fires were still burning and it was deemed that no life could have existed. Gigantic efforts were made to extinguish the fire. It was after three o' clock before this was achieved.

Large crowds gathered at the pit head, and the scene was pitiable.

One woman gazed at the lifeless body of her husband. It was feared that she lost her faculties, at all events she had to be forcibly removed from the scene like some demented person. Another woman, rushed from home nearby to the pit, shouting with anguish in her voice *"Where's my lad, Where's my lad"?*

Those in charge informed her that he was still in the pit and as yet had not been accounted for. Probably the informant tried in his way to instil some pity and a modicum of hope that he may be alive. Words could not comfort her however, for she was still frantic with fear and kept repeating, *"Oh my poor lad! My poor lad!"*.

Some of the bodies were frightfully disfigured, and in some instances the limbs had been severed and lost. One poor man had lost both his arms and both his legs all that remained was the trunk. Such had been the force of the explosion. Women fainted, men turned away horrified at the sights that met their eyes as they endeavoured to identify their loved ones.

The cause of this holocaust was attributed to shot firing.

Seventy seven lamps were given out, only 15 were returned.

The Sofa of Genesis and the stamp of Genius.

Reggie Pepper was an enigma. Aloof almost taciturn, a boy that had put away childish things. Although only a few months older than Charlie, he was never seen with the gang but would speak to Charlie on the rare occasions he was seen in the street. He was a sturdy lad with a mop of black curly hair. His head was rather large and above the normal size. The eyes appeared to be black and seem to glitter like pieces of coal. The Pepper family were again not of the same ilk as their neighbours.
Reggie indeed was a loner and somewhat of a dreamer. The mystery that surrounded him was made even worse by the fact that he did not attend the same school as Charlie. Every one assumed it was because he was being educated at his frequent visits to Reformatory. His incarceration in this establishment was due to numerous felonious crimes, namely, stealing not of money or other mundane articles, but of coils of wire, angle iron, pieces of machinery or anything to do with electrical and mechanical engineering. Indeed it was a very strange if not a weird vice for a lad of this age. Charlie was soon to find the answer.

One afternoon returning from school, alone for once because he had also been on an errand; the gang returning home without him. The street was deserted and turning the corner collided with Reggie. They both smiled at one another and Reggie's eyes seemed to glitter more brightly.

"'ello Reggie'', Charlie greeted him warmly.

"'ello,'' Reggie answered rather shyly and smiled.

"Would yer, would yer like ter see something special?''

Charlie was taken by surprise, for all the years he had known him they had only greeted each other with a cursory nod.

"Ah, yes. When did yer come wom?'' Charlie asked a bit embarrassed for what to say.

"This mornin' ''. Reggie replied. *"This was fer me third tarme yer know. I dunner like that place."*

"Wey do yer do it then. ? Yer know wot ah mean, getting things and

53

getting caught ?''.

Reggie did not answer for a moment or two, turned and started to walk to where he lived. Charlie thought he had been to impertinent in his questioning on such a delicate subject.

"Are yer comin'?'' Reggie asked at last turning to see if Charlie was following him.

"Ah'', He replied hurrying to catch up.

"The reason I do it'' Reggie continued. *"Is ah conna afford ter buy the things ah need. Things ah need fer me projects''*.

"Projects?'' Queried Charlie. *"Wot d'yer mean ?''*.

"Ah'll show yer'' Answered Reggie *"That's if yer interested ?''*.

They entered the front door that opened into the parlour. The wallpaper was peeling off the walls. The floors were bare quarried tiles and dirty. No curtains hung on the unwashed windows. The room was void of furniture, except along one wall was the sofa. A ray of sunshine at that moment illuminated the sombre room. A solitary beam had struggled through the dirty window and displayed, like a floodlight, a work of art. Charlie stood with mouth agape amazed by the spectacle that stood in this unkempt bare room. It was entirely covered with intricate carvings. The centre of the back was the sun surrounded by the planets, on one side was Adam on the other, Eve with a tree bearing the forbidden fruit, and all around them were the birds of the air and animals. The legs were serpents twisting upwards to the arms with mouths open as though ready to strike. No detail had been spared or overlooked. The serpents skin, the birds wings and feathers, the animals fir had been painstakingly recorded.

"Well?'' Asked Reggie. *"Wot's think of it ?''*

"It's. It's wonderful. It's luvely'' Charlie answered his eyes not leaving the masterpiece. *"Who made it?. Oose done o' the carvin' ?''*

"Me faither'' said Reggie with pride. *"An' that inna every thin' ''*. With this he bent down and took from under the sofa a wooden box *"Look at thase''* He said. It was full of carvings of more birds . *"Goo on pick one up''*. Charlie did has he was told

"Cor!'' He exclaimed *"Thee look real dunner thee? It must 'ave taken 'im ages ter mak thase''*.

54

"It did" Said Reggie *"Me faither did it o' wi' a sixpenny penknife from Woolworth's.*

"Gerra way wi' yer! A tanner penknife from Woolie's?"

"It's true" A tanner penknife. This 'ere".

He took from the box the knife, the blade almost worn away with constant honing and use.

"It took me faither six years ter do it, but he just did'ner 'ave time ter complete it"

"Wey?" asked Charlie.

"'E died" replied Reggie.

"When?" Charlie asked his eyes never leaving the knife.

"Some years agoo. Thee were a big fo' and 'e were trapped dine the pit at Wolstanton. It were nearly a wick before thee got to 'im."

"Was 'e d'jed?" Asked Charlie"

"Oh ah, 'e musta suffocated yer see, because thee was no air left ".

"Crikey!" Exclaimed Charlie.

"And this", said Reggie, taking another object from under the sofa, *"Is another unfinished carving 'e was doin' waiting to be rescued. It inna finished, probably cus 'is lamp went out or he died fer want of air. Thee said thee funt 'im wi' it in 'is 'ands wi' the knife 'e 'd carved this with".* The unfinished carving was of a boys head, an uncanny likeness of his youngest son, Reggie. It had been carved from a piece of a pit prop. Reggie placed the knife with reverence back in the box, and took out a piece of paper which he carefully unfolded.

"'E wrote a bit of a poem about the sofa. Would yer like me ter read it.?"

"Yes, ah would" replied Charlie. He was awe struck now at the masterpiece, and the story of the sculptor's demise. Reggie held up the piece of paper close to his face and cleared his throat:

"Bless O Lord this work I pray,
For I have in my humble way,
Tried to copy what You did. No more.
In six days You did but labour
And created Heaven, earth and seas,

All that in there is, even the bees.
I have taken six long years.
With blood sweat and tears,
To carve and fashion this piece of wood,
I only hope it will be understood.
On the seventh year I must rest
From my labour. You will know I've done my best.

Reggie lowered the paper and folded it with reverence. Tears welled in his eyes then ran slowly down his face. He sniffed with impatience as though ashamed of his weakness, placed the paper in the box and, with the cuff of his jacket wiped away the tears off his cheeks. Silence reigned for several moments, both boys' standing with solemn faces looking at the work of art.

"Thee faither", said Charlie at last, *"Must o' bin a bit of a poet as well Reggie"*

"Ah eh were a clever mon eh were" Reggie answered with another sniff. The ray of sunshine that had illuminated the room disappeared as the clouds obscured the sun leaving the room in semi-darkness. Charlie shivered as though he felt a presence in this sombre place.

In the weeks that followed, Reggie showed his new found friend some of the projects he had been working on, and the reason why he had been sent to reformatory school so many times. Charlie was amazed at this poor boy's knowledge and genius. New words, new names entered Charlie's vocabulary, that remained with him always.

Some months after their first meeting, Reggie was incarcerated again, this time he was sent to Borstal for stealing wire and other equipment. He tried to escape from this harsh and cruel environment, unfortunately he fell some forty feet crashing through a glass veranda. This was nearly the end of poor Reggie and he spent the rest of his sentence in the institutions hospital. Charlie met him on his return home, and was rather saddened by his appearance. He seemed subdued, the gleam had vanished from his eyes and he was almost moribund. Only a few words were exchanged and it was the last time he saw him alive.

A few days later Reggie was dead. He had drunk, it was said, some spirits of salts, a very corrosive substance used for cleaning metal prior to soldering. An accident or intentional?

We shall never know. But it was a horrible painful death.

What fame would this brilliant mind could have achieved in different circumstances. Another Faraday, Rutherford, Lodge, Mitchell perhaps, again we shall never know.

The sofa of Genesis? It was sold at an auction, to whom no one can remember, perhaps given pride of place in some stately home or in a museum somewhere for all to see its beauty and artistry. The creator's name.....Anonymous.

Mossfield Explosion 1889.

At 3.45 a.m. on Wednesday October 16th. an explosion occurred at the Mossfield Colliery, known as 'Old Sal'. The noise was heard far and wide, and relatives and friends of the miners, were soon making their way to the pit head. The scene was heart rending. The murky atmosphere and the periodical outbursts of rain, crowds of people with anxiety on their faces straining their eyes at every cage that came up the shaft lent an eeriness to the macabre scene. The bodies were taken to the lamp house to be identified, before being taken to their homes. A sight terrible to witness.

Exploring parties had been at work since the explosion, and as they returned, despairing enquiries were made by the relatives and loved ones of the missing men.

There was doubt at this time that anyone could still be alive, the workings were of awful devastation. One explorer stated that the charred remains of his comrades were found in all parts of the pit. They were covered with dust and dirt, and others not so mutilated had met their death by suffocation. After the 10th body had been recovered it was considered to abandon the recovery fearing another explosion would occur.

The last body to be brought up was Isaac Derricot aged 60 of East Vale. He left a wife and six daughters and five sons. His body according to the medics was ''Mummified''. It seemed that he must have been shot along the roadway like a cannon ball by the force of the explosion.

It appeared that all the survivors had been working in the Cockshead seam. From enquiries made of these men, the first indication, that anything was wrong was that they heard a dull heavy sound like thunder. They had all been thrown to the ground by a force, which was followed by a cloud of thick dust. Fearing the worst they made for the pit bottom. Their lamps had gone out and found great difficulty in groping their way in complete darkness. They stumbled over Jesse Smith who was suffering from the effects of the after damp and other injuries and they assisted him to the pit bottom. Another man they found lying near to a dead pony was named Dennis and was terribly injured. The man Jesse Smith, was taken to the cottage hospital, he was badly burned, several ribs had been displaced and had pierced a lung and was blind. He was 19 years of age.

George Hewitt known as Zulu by his workmates had a remarkable escape. He was working near to a return airway door. The force of the explosion blew the door down on top of him. He stuffed his cap into his mouth to minimise the effects of the after damp, and he managed to wriggle from under the heavy door and make his way to the pit bottom. He was immediately drawn to the surface. After a rest he volunteered to join the rescue party.

A Clergyman stood amongst his rough collier audience and prayed earnestly for the preservation of the rescuers.

Mr. Potts the manager, selected six men to accompany him and his under-manager Mr. Fletcher, under-ground. After awhile they brought out several men alive. Mr. Potts said that the dead were lying about in heaps. They descended again bringing more bodies to the surface. At 10 a.m the operation was suspended , because of the fear of another explosion. The cause of the disaster, was in the opinion of Mr. Potts, spontaneous combustion.

The scene in the lamphouse where the identification of the bodies took place was terrible. Frank Emery aged 50, it had been his first shift at the pit, his head had been blown to pieces. Next to him was a youth who had been badly burned and must have suffered very much before dying. He was first identified as William Bell of Sandford Hill, but later his poor father claimed him as his son, John Shenton aged 18 of Dividy Lane. The father of James James aged 23, and Thomas James aged 18, bore up well, but his daughter threw herself across the dead body of her youngest brother, Thomas, and could not be comforted.

So much could be told of the heartache of the relatives of the sixty six men and boys that perished on that early Wednesday morning on October 16th. 1889. Twenty five pit ponies also perished.

If this explosion had happened on the day shift, twice as many men would have been at work, and the likely death toll could have been doubled.

"In the midst of Life ✝ we are in Death."

In Memory of the

Sixty-Six Colliers

WHO LOST THEIR LIVES IN THE

Mossfield Colliery Explosion, Longton,

Wednesday, October 16th, 1889.

In perfect health they left their homes.
Not knowing that their time was come ;
A sudden change upon them fell,
No time to bid their friends farewell.

JACOB BATH, 33.	ARTHUR FLETCHER, 26.	GEORGE RATCLAFFE, 31.
THOMAS BOUGH, 21,	FREDERICK HARES.	WILLIAM SALTER, 48.
THOMAS BRADSHAW.	JONATHAN HARDING, 25	GEORGE STEELE, 14
WILLIAM BREWOOD, 29	WM. HENRY HULME, 27.	JOHN STEELE, 16.
JOHN BALL, 36	DAVID HULME, 23.	JOHN SMITH, 18.
NOAH BALL, 41.	DAVID HUGHES, 65.	WILLIAM SMITH, 16.
JOSEPH BULL, 58.	WILLIAM HURST. 49.	WILLIAM SIMPSON
JOB BULL, 27.	JAMES HULSE, 26.	GEORGE SALT, 42.
JOSEPH BULL, 25.	WM. B. HEATH. 34.	HERBERT SELLERS
WILLIAM BULL, 19.	JOHN HALL, 16.	JOHN SHENTON, 18.
JAMES BAILEY, 16.	WM. JOHNSTONE, 34.	THOMAS SHERWIN, 25.
THOMAS BROUGH.	RICHARD JONES, 24.	SAMUEL SHERWIN, 18.
JOHN BRADBURY	JAMES B. JAMES, 23.	CHARLES SHERWIN, 21
WILLIAM BURGESS, 40.	THOMAS JAMES, 18.	FRANCIS M. SHAW. 26.
JOSEPH COTTON, 26.	CHARLES JENKINS.	JOHN TOMLINSON, 32.
HENRY CALCOTT, 25.	EDWARD JONES, 30.	EDWARD TOWNSEND, 26.
ISAAC DERRICOTT, 60.	WILLIAM LAWSON, 18.	THOMAS WALKER, 26.
ALBERT EDWARDS.	JOHN MOORE, 31. .	SAMPSON WEDGWOOD 28.
GEORGE EDWARDS. 42.	THOMAS MOFFATT.	SPENC'R WHITEHURST, 24
FRANK EMERY, 50.	EVAN PRICE, 27.	JOHN WILLIAMS, 17.
WILLIAM FARRELL, 23.	WILLIAM H. PLANT, 35.	GEORGE WILSON.
JOSEPH EDWARDS. 57.	SYDNEY RUTTER, 30.	HENRY WOOD, 20.

" WATCH : FOR IN SUCH AN HOUR AS YE THINK NOT THE SON OF MAN COMETH.'

The memorial cross, in Longton
Stoke on Trent, cemetery
inscribed on the plinth are the
names of the men and boys who
lost their lives at "Old Sal" in 1889

Into the Depths of Despair.

They had been doing it for years, having the last few minutes of fun before descending into the bowels of the earth. The young youths on the night shift sitting on the pavement just out side the gates of Hanley Deep Pit, wolf whistling the girls as they passed on their way to the dance hall or just walking past in the High street that is now Town Road. Their elder brothers did it, and probably their fathers too, a kind of tradition that was handed down. A gang of about 20 youths having a last cigarette until urged by the overman to get down the pit. Reluctantly they would rise, switch on their heavy electric hand lamps and walk slowly to the shaft. Some of the fortunate ones saying farewell to the girls who had succumbed to their banter and charm. One or two perhaps were their girl friends who they were courting and had missed their evening out at the cinema or a dance because they were on the night shift.

Jack and George, mates since childhood, and now working at Hanley 'big un' had met Anne and Nellie at a soiree, known locally as the 'Monkey Run' , in Piccadilly in Hanley, a few weeks earlier.
Anne seemed besotted with Jack, whilst Nellie was somewhat indifferent to George, and was just sort of tagging along because Anne was her best friend, and only went with George to please her.
"See yer on Saturday Anne outside the Capital at 6 o' clock"
Said Jack, kissing her briefly on the mouth. Anne tried to embrace him but he resisted.
"No duck yer'll get yer coat dirty, ah'm covered in coal dust."
He smiled and she giggled. *"Night sweetheart and be careful"*.
George was looking a bit forlorn and had hoped that Nellie would kiss him too. *"Ta-ra,"* was all she said and turned and walked away.
"Ah dunna think she larks may", said George.
"Wey, wot makes thee see that?" asked Jack.
"Well yo' con see fer thee sel' 'er even wunna let may kiss 'er. Not lark Anne, ah bet 'er'd do anythin' fer they, 'er would". George said mournfully as they stepped into the cage.

62

Saturday night came and the two pit lads, dressed in their best, awaited at the entrance of the Capital Cinema.

"Thee 'r late anna thee ", said George looking at his wrist watch, *"It's a quarter past six. If thee asks mey ah dunner think thee 'r coming"*.
"Thee wull. thee 'll bey 'ere any minute mark ma words. " replied Jack. Another five minutes went by and the two girls came in sight. *"Hello' Jack"*, greeted Anne *" I 'm sorry we 're late "*, she took his arm in hers and walked into the foyer. George nodded to Nellie and hoped that she would take his arm, but she just walked with him to the pay box.

The usherette led them with the help of her torch to their seats in the one and nines. It was unfortunate that there was not room for the two couples to sit on the same row. There were two seats together and immediately behind was another two.

"We 'll sit in these two and those two con sit behind ", said Nellie, taking hold of Anne's arm.

"No I want to sit with Jack ", shrugging Nellie's arm off her, *"You sit with George "*.

With this she took Jack's arm and made for the two vacant seats. Nellie reluctantly, with George in tow, sat in the seats immediately behind. It seemed in no time at all, Jack had his arm around Anne, her head resting on his shoulder. George, not to be outdone and following his mates lead attempted to do the same.

"And what do you think you 're doing "? Nellie asked angrily removing poor George's arm.

The offer of ice cream during the interval was also rejected, and George sat through the programme thoroughly dejected.

The programme over, the two couples made their way to the girls homes. Jack and Anne walking arm in arm with George and Nellie walking solemnly, apart behind. They reached the street where they lived, Nellie bade them *"Good night"*, and left. George hands in pockets, shuffled his feet, embarrassed no doubt by Nellie's quick departure. *"Good naight "*, he said at last and walked away leaving the two who it seemed were anxious to resume their love making.

Jack and George met again on the following Monday, down the pit on the day shift. During 'snappin' time they discussed the events of the week-end.

"Ah serpose yo were wi'Anne on Sunday weren't yer"? George asked taking a bite out of his bacon and cheese sandwich.

"Ah", replied Jack.

"W'ere did yer goo?"

"In the afternoon wey went dine 'Anley Park and then after tea wey went ter the pictures". Replied Jack.

"Did 'er goo wi' 'er"? George asked with surliness in his voice.

"Oo dust mane, 'er"?

"They knowst oo ah mane, 'er, Nellie."

"Na, mey and Anne. Wey went on ah own", said Jack closing his snappin' tin and taking a drink of water from his bottle.

"Wee did 'er goo then"? Enquired George.

"Oo?"

"Wot's up wi' they"? At in love o' wot. Cos'na answer a simple question? They knowst oo ah mane. 'Er Nellie!" George exclaimed angrily.

"Ow should ah know weer she went?" Jack answered, *"Er's nowt ter do wi' mey. Any road up, ah thought 'er was thar lady"*.

"Mar lady! Mar lady!" George shouted standing up and gathering up his snappin' tin, water bottle and lamp.

"Er conna stand the sight o 'mey fer some reason", George stood for a few moments looking into the darkness of the crut, the light from his lamp caught the queer glint in his eyes.

"Ah love 'er thee knowst Jack. Ah'd do ite fer 'er", his voice had softened now. Jack looked up at him and thought he was going to break down and cry. He was about to commiserate with his friend, but George, at that moment, walked away into the darkness.

Even on the pavement outside the Ideal, the dance hall in the High Street now the Town Road, you could hear the small band playing "There'll be no rain down Apple Blossom Lane" which seemed to be beckoning the young men and girls to enter its portals and dance the evening away. Anne and Jack were already there in each others arms, so was Nellie in someone else's arms. The surliness in her face was no longer there, she was smiling and looking amorously in her partners eyes. The dance floor was full of couples with the usual wallflowers and others around its periphery.

Suddenly, there was a movement in the entrance. A youth, unkempt, his face white and eyes staring, fought his way to the dance floor. Voices were raised in annoyance against this contemptuous youth, but were totally ignored by him. It was George, his staring eyes scanned the scene before him, and in a trice, ran forward shifting everyone in his path. The band high on the rostrum, noticing that there was some thing amiss, stopped playing and the couples ceased to dance. George had reached his goal. Nellie and her new boy friend. She looked at the apparition with a mixture of annoyance and fear.

"Dance wi' me"! It croaked.

"Get off and leave me alone"! She almost screamed.

"Come and dance wi' me please", George implored.

"Will yer get off and stop botherin' me." Nellie shouted. The colour of her face had taken on a reddish hue and was plainly embarrassed because of all the eyes of the people were staring at her.

"Dance wi' me", again George implored, his arms now outstretched to take her.

"Get off!" Nellie screamed. *"Get off, I hate the sight of you"*.

Her gallant escort, took a grip on George's arms.

"'Ers towd they ter get off"! So, sod off!"

George's eyes pierced his rival's, and for a few moments stood transfixed. Shaking his arms free he then delivered a right cross to his rivals jaw, knocking him to the floor. Nellie screamed, and so did many others. George took hold of her and embraced her.

"Dance wi' me", he said softly. Nellie screamed again, and fought to release herself from his embrace. Jack, thought it time to intervene, and went to Nellie's aid.

"Come on George lad, leave her bey", he said taking hold of his arms, *"Come on wi' mey youth"*.

"There'll be no work fer yo lot ter naight"

George turned. *"Oh it's they"*, he said, *"Ah only want 'er ter dance wi' me"*. With this he released his grip on Nellie.

"Ah love 'er thee knowst Jack. Ah'd do owt fer 'er. But 'er dunna want mey. Wey Jack, wey?" He bowed his head as though in shame and started to sob.

"Come on youth" said Jack, *"Let's tack thee wom"*

They moved slowly off the dance floor, the dancers making way.

The band started to play again but over the lilting melody the shrill voice of Nellie screaming *"'Eh's bloody cracked eh is, wants puttin' awee, the soft sod!"*

George half turned and looked at her, tears streaming down his face.

"Come on George lad, tack ner notice. 'Er inna woth it".

With a cry like some deranged being, he ran from the dance hall, with Jack in hot pursuit. He ran along the High street and paused momentarily staring down at the lads sitting on the pavement outside Hanley Deep Pit. *"There'll be no work fer yo lot ter naight"*, he said quietly, and with a queer sort of laugh he ran through the gates to the downcast shaft stopping just for a moment to look round. then vaulted over the rails into the dark abyss below. Jack was to late to stop him. *"My God"*, he said as he peered down the shaft and listened to the diminishing scream.

Strike Of 84/85.

The miners' strike of 1984-85 was the longest coal strike in the history of the mining industry. It was the most costly and bloodiest. The most extraordinary thing about this conflict, it was not just about money and conditions, but a fight for their jobs and the life of whole communities. It was not like the old days, when miners' fought the against the pit owners, for demanding their pound of flesh. This fight was against the government, the philosophy of Margaret Thatcher and the ruthless American trouble shooter she employed to try and annihilate the National Union of Minewokers. To her advantage, she used the full force of the police, the press and the media.

At the beginning of the year long strike, there were about 5800 miners' working at the remaining five North Staffordshire collieries, Holditch, Wolstanton, Silverdale, Florence, and Hem Heath.

It was in October 1983, the National Union of Mine workers called for an overtime ban as a protest against the National Coal Board's, 5.2 percent pay offer. The reasons for the rejection of the offer was two fold. The rate of inflation was higher than the pay which effectively meant a cut in pay, and more importantly, to resist the threat of more pit closures. Closures of those pits which the pundits called 'uneconomic pits'.

By January 1984, the overtime ban was causing some difficulty, not only for the Coal Board, but also for the Unions. The winders, who operate the cages, belonged to their own Winders Branch, this was part of the Power Group. There was deep rooted differences between the underground workers and themselves. Although the winders had once worked underground, and had special training they thought they were a cut above the miners'. They took a decision at their branch not to take part in the overtime ban causing great dissension amongst themselves and the industry. Pickets were set up at the pit gates. A strong police presence was felt, giving a taste of what was to come.

The outcome of the overtime ban had certainly made its mark. The N.C.B admitted that output had been seriously affected. At Hem Heath production fell from 31000 tonnes to 17000 tonnes per week. Holditch

A strong police presence (Evening Sentinel)

The police were now organised to prevent picketing (Evening Sentinel)

The last great battle of Orgreave, 18 th. June 1984.
Arthur Scargill battered but not defeated

"Where's your black hat Neil?" (Evening Sentinel)

went on all out strike, when four men did repairs without Union agreement.

The Coal Board used the media in their propaganda, to show photographs indicating that, the Wolstanton pit was in a 'Hell of a mess'. They inferred that if the men did not go back quickly the mine would be irretrievably damaged and that they would be forced to close it down. Joe Wills the President of the North Staffs N.U.M. arranged for a deputation to go down the pit. They examined the whole of the pit and disproved the propaganda.

Mark Fisher the local M.P. gave regular support and even attended the picket lines. *"There were many examples during the dispute of civil liberties being infringed and of the police assuming extraordinary powers over the control of communities"*, he said, and went on to tell about his telephone that had been tapped. *"You can have no proof that the phone was tapped but I suspect it was. On occasions, to miners' leaders, they would say afterwards that the information they may have given me on the phone, was responded to with amazing speed by the local police"*. He recalled that his wife received a threatening phone call when a third voice broke into the conversation and said: *"Don't worry Mrs. Fisher, we've got this mans phone number and we will be dealing with it"*.

The Coal Board, (true to the forecast of Arthur Scargill, President of the N.U.M,) announced the closure of Cortonwood Colliery in Yorkshire, and four more pits in the country. This announcement and the threat of more closures without union agreement sparked off a full scale strike.

So it began in the early days of March 1984, and so did the confrontations of the two main belligerents, Scargill and Macgregor.

The leaders of the Power Group and the Midlands N.U.M. demanded a National ballot and that the pay rise, and pit closures be kept as a separate issue. In March, flying pickets were at Lea Hall in Rugeley, and Littleton in Cannock. Men from Yorkshire picketed the night shift at Hem Heath. From the first, bus drivers from the Potteries Motor Traction Co. (P.M.T.) refused to cross picket lines and dropped their fares at the gates, so that the strike breakers had to walk through the picket lines. The P.M.T were penalised for this action. The Coal Board never renewed their contract. From then on there was no normal working at any of the North Staffordshire pits. Violence, and intimidation by the police had started with a vengeance. Even the strike breakers were subjected to a search. On more than one occasion, police raided social and working men's clubs, looking, it was said, for 'militants'. At Hem Heath one man was being beaten mercilessly, and six of his mates went to his aid, and were subsequently arrested.

By the end of March there was only a few men at work in North Staffs. The Weighbridge office at Hem Heath was firebombed so that lorries could not be weighed. The National Union of Railwaymen and others refused to move any coal. The Coal Board were now desperate to move coal, and it hired 'Cowboy' contractors with dangerously old vehicles, (the police ignoring the illegal aspects).

In April, about 70 men went to work at Hem Heath, out of a work force of 1700. At Silverdale, 50 out of 800 and 10 out of 900 at Wolstanton.

The Police were now organised to try and prevent picketing. Photographs and videos of the pickets were being taken. The number of arrests were increased and so did the intimidation.

Hardship was beginning to bite even at this early stage, not only to the miners' and their families but to the local economy. The loss of income was in the region of £2 million. Closure of some shops was a common place. Banks and building societies were concerned about loans and mortgages, and the effects of the squeeze had on the borrowers.
A special conference on the 19th. April made the decision that there would be no special ballot. It was also made clear that the N.U.M. would fight to the finish.

Donations began to come in from a wide range of people. From Michelin workers, the Indian Communities, French dockers and miners' (who by the way were experiencing pit closures). Miners' from the Pas du Nord who brought food and money said that they had worked in as many as nine different pits. The pits closing one after the other, forcing the miners to move from pit to pit. The help from these sectors of industry and local communities, played an important part in sustaining the strikers. Food centres operated in the area manned mainly by the miners' wives, the women's support groups. This support gave their partners, the will to carry on through courage and determination. They too were not left unscathed by the police. There were many incidents around the coalfields where theses women were subjected to violence and intimidation. Police arrested women on a Nottingham picket line.

Support for the strike grew as the populace realised the importance of the dispute. On the 5th. of May, the North Staffs Trades Council organised a rally. About 4000 people came and the 'May Day' march in Stoke-on-Trent. It was the biggest demonstration since the 1926 coal strike. Speakers at the rally included Brenda Proctor from the women's' support group, and the local Members of Parliament, John Golding and Mark Fisher. Political differences were swept aside when the Stoke Miners' support Group was organised. Members from the Labour Party, New Communist Party, Communist Party of Great Britain, C.N.D, Friends of the Earth and others, concentrated all their organising skills to raise funds. At first permits for collection points were refused by the Council, but after repeated pressure and correspondence they relented.

The Groups efforts raised about £10,000. Even with permission from the Council they were harassed by the police, some members were arrested and the money confiscated.

Arthur Scargill attended a meeting at the Victoria Hall in Hanley on the 25th. May together with Mark Fisher and Jim Colgan. This meeting gave a tremendous boost to the cause. The next day a gift of £800 worth of food from the workers of Rolls Royce at Crewe.

By June more men reported for work, the strikers continued the picketing . Most strikers were at the pit gates by 5.15 a.m. On the night shift they were often joined by women from the support groups. Three N.U.M officials were suspended from office at the Lea Hall pit in South Staffs for supporting the return to work, and one of them threatened to take the N.U.M to court. After the strike, he was rewarded by the Coal Board for being a turncoat. He was given an industrial relations job.

The Power group finally made the strike official. Roy Ottey told them of his decision. *"I was the one who had to go and read the decision to the chanting crowd, and I have to say it was the most humiliating experience in my whole union career. The 'lobbyists' chants changed to cheers as they listened"*, he said. As a result of this decision the Power Group were now able to authorise the expenditure of funds for picket duty. The funds which until this time had come from Midland Area Funds.

Orgreave saw the bloodiest confrontations in an industrial dispute since the 20s. and the 30s. The conflict was an example of class warfare at its worst. It was not just a case of stopping the supplies of coal and coke to Scunthorpe. It was an attempt by the government to deploy highly trained riot police to prove to the populace, that picketing could not succeed.

The last great battle at Orgreave was on the 18th. June when 5000 pickets were confronted by an equal number of police with riot shields with the backing of dogs and horses.

After this battle the government decided to engineer a drift back to work. The National Working Miners Committee was organised by a non-miner, David Hart. With the blessing of Thatcher and Macgregor, and in its name, a series of legal actions were taken against the N.U.M. These legal actions caused the sequestration of its funds and the appointment of a receiver. The government then launched a propaganda offensive, stating that the strike was only continuing by fear and intimidation. This subterfuge increased the momentum of police power. They invaded the mining communities, sometimes just to get a single scab to work and other raids to show their prowess. Fifty police officers charged into an area 'on the double' and entered private property without any invitation or course. Mining areas were put in a state of siege.

Christmas time was nigh and more men returned to work. For the rest it seemed that the season of goodwill would be one of heartbreak. More bad news reached the area; the death of a Taxi driver.

A major event for the area was the meeting in Stoke town hall with Arthur Scargill and Neil Kinnock the Labour party leader.

A warm reception was given to Scargill, contrasting the very lukewarm response to Kinnock. The speech by Kinnock was thought by many to be for consumption by the media and for his own ego, and not for the miners cause. The result was that many loyal Labour supporters were disillusioned.

Although there was heckling at the meeting, and despite the gravity of the situation, there was a modicum of humour.

Kinnock said that the strike was not like a cowboy film in which the good guys wore white hats and the bad guys wore black hats.

He was interrupted by a loud voice from the audience: *"Where's your black hat Neil"*?

Donations for the Christmas appeal were now pouring in, and the women from the support group were spending most of their time dealing with them. So Christmas was not as bad, as had been anticipated. At least not for the children, due to the generosity of the people and support groups from all over the country.

By the end of January the N.C.B claimed that only 463 men were still on strike in North Staffs, and that production was almost back to normal. This fierce and bloody struggle came to an end in March 1985. A battle with no victors because neither the miners' nor the coal industry gained anything from it. It proved one thing, that the prediction of

75

Scargill would come true. The prediction that, pit closures and whole communities split asunder, and the annihilation of a great industry. An industry whose people had helped to make this nation of ours, once one of the greatest nations on earth.

It would take a tome to record all the events of this great struggle, to show for all time the deprivation and despair, the sadness it left in its wake. The wounds of battle will be remembered for generations to come.

And so it came to pass, out of the 350 known collieries that once operated in the North Staffordshire coalfield, there is, at the time of writing, **none**. For on the 3rd. of December 1993, which should be recorded in history books as 'Black Friday', the last deep mine in North Staffordshire, Silverdale Colliery, closed, ending an era of great tradition.

A Prayer For Christmas

The headline on the 23rd. December 1938 in a newspaper, in bold black type read:

HOPE IS RUNNING OUT FOR THE TRAPPED MEN.

It as now been three days since the rock fall entombed three miners, and reports from the pit head this morning gave little hope that they are still alive. But, said the spokesman, every effort is being made to reach them, with teams working round the clock. The three miners are:-
Jack Thomas, aged 30, Collier. Married with one daughter.
Harry Williams, aged 23, Loader. Single.
Thomas Rowley, aged 14 haulage hand,

Harry Williams was to be married at Christmas to his childhood sweetheart Anne Grainger. Relatives and friends of Miss Grainger have tried to persuade her to leave the pit head where she has been since Tuesday in a state of shock. For nearly three days she has remained, indifferent to the inclement weather awaiting for the news that her loved one would soon be rescued. She now seems to be in a state of torpidity, muttering at times incoherently, and sometimes through the anguish a pitiful cry of: *"I want my Harry. Please, please take me to him"*. On several occasions she has had to be restrained from trying to gain access to the cage. Doctor Robinson who has been at the scene since yesterday, is very concerned for her health and has suggested that she must be removed, and forcibly if need be.

Three thousand feet below the surface and some three miles inbye and behind tons of rock, the three miners' squat in this tomb, exhausted by the effort of moving and ridding the rock to try and escape. The want of sustenance, food and water is beginning to tell. The lights of their oil lamps have been turned very low to conserve the precious oil, knowing as they do that in a short time they will be in total darkness. The air is becoming stale, this they know will not last many more hours.

Harry laboriously rose to his feet and moved to the fall of rock. With
some effort he took up in his raw and bleeding hands a large piece and
threw it behind him.

"*Wot tryin' ter do 'Arry?*" Asked Jack.

Harry turned with anger in his eyes,

"*Wot the 'ell dust think ah'm doin'? Ah conna sit 'ere doin'
nowt*".

"*Look mate ah've towd thee, it's useless. O' they't doin is
usin' up air. Wey o want ter get ite. Thee anna forgot us, thee'll be
through any tarme. So sit thee sel dine*", said Jack

Harry reluctantly did as he was told,

"*Ah've got ter bey ite Jack, thee knowst ah've promised ter
wed Anne on Christmas Eve*". He said softly. "*I wonder wot dee it is,
it inna Christmas Eve is it Jack?*"

"*Nah, not yet. Dunna fret youth, thee'll 'ave us ite in tarme
mark me words*", Jack replied.

"*Ah promised ah Ken, eh's me little brother, ter tak 'im up
McIlroys, th' big shop up 'Anley ter see Santa*" said Tommy.

"*Good lad*" said Jack. "*Dust believe in Santa?*"

"*Nah*", replied Tommy, "*But ah young un does, eh's only
five*".

"*Ah remember wen ah were a lad, a bit younger than you
Tommy, it were abite ninetane twenty two. Me faither tuk us young
uns, me two brothers and little sister, ter Stoke Station ter see Santa
arrive be train. Lord Mayor were theer an 'undreds o' folk. Thee wer
a an army band pleein' an 'e got into a open coach pulled by two jet
black 'osses wi' wate plumes on th' yeds. Thee set off fer 'Anley wi'
thray men in front carryin' a banner with th' words 'Santa Claus is
coming after us to McIlroy's. Wey o follered 'im ter 'Anley weer
'undreds o' folk wer weetin'. Ah've never sain a site lark it, ah an
never will agen, ah dunner serpose.*"

"*Did yer ever tak yower little girl ter see Santa, Jack?*"
Tommy asked.

"*Oh ah, ah took 'er last year, it wer a tanner ter sey 'im in 'is grotto an 'e gave ler a little toy. Ah've promised ter tak 'er this year an o',* "Replied Jack.

"*Dyer like Christmas Jack?*" asked Tommy.

"*Like Christmas lad? Cus ah do. It's magical, mysterious lark. An' of course an 'e wer born, Jesus Christ, the son o' God*"

"*Ah know Jesus wer born, But wots mean- magical?*" Asked Tommy.

"*Well it's different from other tarmes of th' year. Folk wishin' yer well a feelin o' good will, an most o' o-------*

"*Shush!*" *Shush!*" *Harry exclaimed jumping to his feet,* "*Did yer 'ear it?*"

"*Wot?*" asked Jack.

"*Knockin!*" Silence reigned for several moments, ears strained.

"*Theyt 'earin' things,*" remarked Jack.

"*Ah tell thee ah heard knockin'*"

"*Well ah didna. Didst they Tommy?*"

"*Na*"

"*Well yo wunner would yer, blabberin' on abite Christmas. Christ inna 'elpin us is 'e? A dog shudner die lark this---Christ!*" Harry sat down, put his head in his arms and started to sob. At that moment one of the lamps flickered and went out. An eerie silence ensued broken only by an occasional creaking of the remaining timbers supporting the roof.

"*Ah think*", said Jack quietly, "*Ah think lads it's tarme wey said a little prayer . . .*

"*O God, give us, young Tommy, Harry and me, strength and courage to face the next few 'ours in this terrible place, and if Thy will be done, I beseech thee to give comfort to our families that will be left up above for the sake of your son Jesus Christ.*

0 Saviour, Lord, to thee we pray, whose love has kept us safe, protect us through the coming hours, and ever save us by Thy powers. Be with us now, in mercy and spare Thy servants when they cry; Forgive our sins, and receive our prayers, Thy light throughout our darkness give. . .

I con remember some of th' 23 rd. Psalm . . ..

Yea though I walk through the valley of the shadow of death, I will fear no evil. For Thou art with me; Thy rod and Thy staff comfort me. Amen''.

The second lamp flickered and died and they were left in almost complete blackness. Harry felt young Tommy's hand in his, he put his arm around him and drew him close.

"*Jack?'' Asked Tommy in a quiet voice.*

"*Wot son?''*

"*Wot did yer mean wen yer said that Christmas was magic?''*

"*Well, thees a lot a things that 'appen. Thees a part of a poem ah remember that tells some o' the magic o' th' country....*

> *Have you seen by any chance,*
> *The moonbeams an' th' fairies dance,*
> *Beautiful pearls made out of dew,*
> *Flimsy, like gossamer, the spider too*
> *Spins a web for all to see*
> *And wonder at its intricacy.*
>
> *Christmas sometimes brings snow to the ground,*
> *A white mantle silencing all the sound.*
> *Tell tale marks reveal the fox,*
> *A rabbit, a weasel, scampers o'er the rocks.*
> *The vixen coughs, the robin sings,*
> *On Christmas eve the church bell rings,*
> *Calling the people for congregation,*
> *To give thanks for their salvation.''*

"*That's magic Jack''*, whispered Tommy.

"*Ah lad thees a lot more, things wey dunnq appreciate until its t' late''.*

"*Did yer 'ear that? That knockin'. Theer it is agen!''* Exclaimed Harry jumping to his feet and stumbling panic stricken to the fall.

"Ah, ah did", shouted Harry rising to his feet.

"An'mey", shouted Tommy.

The knocking was louder now, and the three answered by shouting.

"Ello" came the voice from beyond, *"Wey'll bey with you soon"*
The three turned and faced each other smiling and then embraced.

"Thank God". Said Jack

"Ah", said Harry,

"It's Magic," said Tommy, *"an' thee Christmas prayer Jack."*
The flame in the last remaining lamp slowly died and they were enveloped in blackness. Their embrace became much tighter.

"Dunna worry lads it wunna bey long". Jack said.

They stepped from the cage, it was dark and it was snowing. The sky was clear and the stars shone brightly. In the distance the church bells peeled merrily. It was Christmas Eve. Young Tommy looked up at Jack smiling,

"It's magic Jack"

"Ah lad". The collier replied, *"And it's Christmas"*.

Anne, her long vigil over, clung to her man sobbing hysterically.

"Thank God", she cried.

81

Shaffalong Coalfield

It is difficult to ascertain at what time coal was first extracted in the Shaffalong area. John Farey, that assiduous researcher, listed in 1810 the following in his list of collieries:-

Crown Point. 1 mile S.W. of Cheddleton, 2nd coal.

Consall Wood 2½ miles S.W. of Cheddleton, 1st coal.

Newstead 1 mile S.S.W. of Cheddleton, 1st. Coal.

Shaffalong ¾ mile S.S.W. of Cheddleton 2nd. Coal.

Wetley Moor (or Handley Ease) 2¾ miles S.W.. of Cheddleton.

Crown Point, Newstead, and Shaffalong can be considered all to be part of the Shaffalong Coalfield, and were obviously being worked at that time.

On the first page of the Cheddleton Parish Register, dated 27th. December 1696, is the entry, *'Susanna Dale daughter of Benjamin Dale of the Coal Pit Ford was baptised'*. The name Coal Pit Ford suggests that mining was taking place in that area at least as early as that time. The house is supposed to have been known by that name when it was built or rebuilt by one Francis Fynney in the middle of the 17th. Century. Both the house and the associated colliery are referred to in an advertisement in the Staffordshire Advertiser dated 18th. December 1802, and the colliery, by then owned by Captain Thomas Powyss, was again advertised to be let on 8th. December, 1849. It is interesting to note that Captain Powyss was in the Dragoon Guards and fought in the Napoleonic War, and a magistrate during the Chartist riots and on the 16th. August 1842, read the Riot Act to a mob in Burslem. With Major Trent the commander of the 2nd Dragoons after repeated warnings and reading of the Riot Act to some 5000 of the mob, the Captain gave the order to *''Clear the streets and Charge''*. The mounted troops attempted to move them by using the flats of their swords, but to no avail. About midday a huge mob from Leek joined them, *"What do you want here?''* Shouted Captain Powys. *''Our rights and liberty, The Charter and more to eat''*. Replied the mob.

The Captain realising that further reasoning was pointless asked the Major to open fire. Joseph Heapy from Leek was killed outright, many were wounded or trampled on by the horses as they fled.

Another story about the Captain is of his macabre death after a confrontation with the witch of Rownall.

The North Staffordshire Field Club Transactions for 1914/15 contains an article by J. T. Stobbs, which quotes that an old mining notebook of the 1770s. The following extracts are taken from it, showing that mining was taking place in the area at that time.

1775 Deadwork at the Ross boring at 1s.4d. per day.

1776 Boring two days, 3 men at 1s.4d. per day and 1 boy at 7d.

12th. October. Deadwork stone getting. Wages at 1s.4d. per day.

1777 9th. May. Heading 125 yards at 8d per yard.

Heading 120 yards at 1s. per yard.

27th. December. Heading 80 yards at 8d. per yard.

1778 Cheese at 4d. per lb. Meal at 1s 0d per peck.

Sod cutting ceremony at Shaffalong

Whether mining was taking place continuously from the 17th. Century to 1849 in the Shaffalong Coalfield or not, is impossible to say. It is likely that several attempts were made to extract coal over the period and that mines were probably operated at least throughout the first half of the century. No record is available of any mining after the advertisement in 1849, and it seems highly probable that the lease was not taken up at that time.

A further attempt to develop the coalfield took place in the early years of the 20th. Century. After optimistic borings by Belgian engineers in 1904, the following report appeared in the Staffordshire Advertiser of 13th. October. 1906.:-

The cutting of the first sod of the new colliery took place on Thursday 11th October, being performed by Mrs. James Meakin.

Over two years ago, three boring operations commenced on the Westwood Manor Estate belonging to Mr. Meakin, one at Shaffalong Farm, one at the base of Susan's Wood, and one near Wetley Church. The three borings almost exactly corresponded and showed five beds of coal in the lower carboniferous series. A valuable Ironstone was also found. Consequently in July last the Westwood Manor Coal and Iron Company Limited was registered with capital of £100,000 in £1 shares to carry on the business of Miners and workers of dealers in coal and iron, and other minerals, coke and patent fuel manufacturers, steelmakers and converters, smelters, quarry owners, engineers, gasmakers etc. and in particular to acquire a lease of minerals under the Westwood Manor estate in Staffordshire.

The Colliery manager was Mr. B. Parker of Wetley Rocks. Mr. E. Marshall Fox was Chairman of the Directors, and Lord Armstrong the Vice Chairman. The other directors were Messrs. Claude Wallace, J .O. Lawson Johnson, T. Blake, J. S. Southwell and W. H. P. Dickson. All seven directors were based in London.

It was reported that the company hoped to commence coal getting after about 12 months, and anticipated being able to raise 1000 tons a day.

The contract for sinking two shafts, 200 yards in depth went to J. Goodwin of Brown Edge, and William Hollinshead of Cheadle, the owner of the notebook quoted previously. The two upper coal beds were not regarded as being of any great commercial value, but the three lower ones were thought to vary from 2 feet 9 inches to 4 feet 5 inches and to consist of exceedingly rich coal.

The brave beginning contrasted sadly with the following report which appeared in the Leek Deanery Magazine of December 1908, under Cheddleton:-

The Shaffalong Pits.

'After sinking two shafts to a considerable depth, one of them being nearly 600 feet down, the Westwood Manor Coal and Iron Company has had to abandon them on account of the water they have found. It is a great pity to have men thrown out of work at this time of year. But most of them may get employment again, as the directors have hopes of starting a brickyard close to the present colliery, and also intend boring again some five hundred yards to the south east of the existing shafts. We admire their hopefulness after meeting such disasters, and trust they will be as successful as they are sanguine'.

Sinking of shaft

85

A marl hole, for marl clay, was dug soon after this time at the side of Brund Lane with a view to brick making, but this never came viable. Since then, few attempts have been made to exploit the coal. In 1909, Thomas Farrell who lived at the Prospect drove in a foot-rail on his land, on the opposite side of the valley to Westwood Manor, but he was unsuccessful. During the 1926 coal strike a little out-cropping was done, but it was unlikely that any good coal was produced. Once the workings had been deserted, the Staffordshire Potteries Water Board purchased them and pumped the offending water out of the shafts for their own use.

Superstitions.

The miner and his family, due to the very nature of his work are very superstitious. These irrational fears have been handed down from one generation to another. In some families have strictly adhered to them, and in some cases they have been an excuse to have a day off work.

Superstition 1. *If a woman asks the time when you are going to work, do not go to work on that day.*

One man I knew lost a weeks work when the same woman accosted him without fail on six consecutive mornings to ask him the time. He remonstrated with her daily to no avail she still chose him to tell her the time, although there were always several others going to the pit she could have asked. So not wanting to tempt fate he kept returning home. Another man when asked the time by a woman, returned to his home to find his wife had invited her paramour to share the bed he had not long vacated. A good or bad omen in this case?

Superstition 2. *Never go to work on New years Day.*

Whether this was an excuse for an extra days holiday to get over the New Year celebrations was never proved, but it certainly came true when the explosion at Sneyd colliery occurred on January 1st. 1942 and 57 men and boys were blasted into eternity. They tempted fate to serve their country in time of war to produce the coal that was badly needed. Just before the stroke of midnight on New Years Eve, putting a piece of coal in his pocket, a miner would go out of the back door and let the New Year in by coming in the front door.

Superstition 3. *To dream of a broken shoe, boot or clog was a sure sign of danger.*

Superstition 4. *To dream of fire is another sign of danger.*

Superstition 5. *To see a bright light in the pit is a sign to get away.*

87

Superstition 6. *To hear a pack of hounds on the way to the pit. It is said that: 'Owd Gabriel is abite'.*

Superstition 7. *To hear a howling dog, you should take off your boot or clog from the left foot, spit upon the sole and place it on the ground bottom upwards and put your foot on the place you spat on.* This would preserve you from danger and stop the dog howling.

Superstition 8. *Never cut your nails on a Friday or a Sunday.*

Superstition 9. *Crossing the path of a cross-eyed woman on his way to the pit was one of the worst omens, and under no circumstances would he go work that day.*
In the home the family would abide by the normal superstitions.

Superstition 10. *Avoid crossing knives, spilling salt, walking under ladders.*

Superstition 11. *Finding a hole in cut bread was greeted with dread a sign of death and a grave.*

Superstition 12. *After giving birth, a woman would not be allowed in another house unless she had been 'Churched'.*

Superstition 13. *When visiting a neighbour, friend or relative, depart by the same door you entered by.*

Superstition 14. *Never put a shoe or boot on the table.*

Superstition 15. *It is believed that the Devil puts his cloven foot upon blackberries on Michaelmas Day, 29th. September.*
None should be gathered after that date, for the berries are cursed and will bring bad luck when eaten. If wine be made it is said will be vinegary.

Superstition 16. *The finger nails of a child was not to be cut until it is twelve months old.*
If done before that time the child will, it is said would become a thief.

Superstition 17. *The palms of the child be washed or wealth would be washed away.*

Superstition 18. *To injure or kill a frog is unlucky.*

Superstition 19. *To throw hair out of doors when combing or cutting their hair, would have an headache or toothache as long as they live.*

Superstition 20. *The rocking of an empty cradle was a sign that the baby would die soon.*

Superstition 21. *If a soot flake hangs from the bars of the grate, it is said that a stranger will come.*
By the clapping of hands and saying the days of the week will tell the day of their arrival when the flake falls off.

Superstition 22. *The fire spitting an ember on to the hearth when a miner was about to leave for the pit would forecast danger and he would not go.*

Superstition 23. *The Boggart of Kidsgrove* is well known amongst the miners' of that area. It was said that it was the soul of a young woman who was brutally murdered near the Harecastle tunnel. She would appear wailing to give a sign that a pit disaster was imminent. This was a proven fact over the years when several such calamities occurred, and to name a few it was said that she appeared on the days on which the Talk o' th' Hill, Bunkers Hill, Birchenwood and Diglake disasters which caused an horrendous loss of lives.

Dust 'Ere.

In 1943 a young man from down south, was elected due to the new law that men reaching call up age for National Service would either serve in the armed services or work in the mines as a Bevin Boy.

After a period of training at the Kemball pit, where he was taught the rudiments of mining particularly safety. He was designated to work at the Sneyd Colliery.

On his first morning, he was waiting at the pit bottom for the overman to tell him what to do, and leaned nonchalantly on a tub full of stone dust. Stone dust as you may know is spread in the workings to stop spontaneous combustion by coal dust.

"They't bey th' Bevin boy. At?" Said the Overman.

"Yes sir" he replied.

"Stee 'ere ah shanna bey long" said the Overman, *"Dust 'ere?"* and then started to walk inbye.

He was a bit surprised at having no one of experience to work with, on his first day but never the less he thought he had been given a task to do what was in his capability. *"Dust here"* that was the overman had told him. He glanced around him and saw a shovel, so he set to work with a will and determination to show that he was not afraid of hard work. He beavered away with the shovel as though his very life depended on it. The main crut was soon filled with fine white dust, so much, that it was impossible to see. He wondered whether maybe he was overdoing it. A muted roar followed by bouts of coughing halted him, deeming it wise to pause in his enthusiastic endeavours.

There emerged from the assimilated blizzard, what looked like the Abominable Snowman. Then it roared. He realised at once that it was the overman.

"Wot th' soddin bloody 'ell at they doin'? Yer daft bat" He demanded angrily.

"I'm dusting here like you told me", he said cringing between bouts of coughing.

"Ah never towd they ter stone dust" he shouted with difficulty. *"Bbut mister you did. The last thing you said was ... Dust here!"*

His endeavours had caused some concern. The stone dust travelled throughout the pit. Some even thought that another explosion had occurred like the one twelve months earlier, and the men were making their way hurriedly to the pit bottom. Even the residents of Burslem thought the same, as the fine white dust billowed up the upcast shaft and settled like snow in the area.

A Visit to the Apendale Small Mines 1993

Hidden beneath, the beautiful valley and hills of Apedale, lies the precious 'black diamond'. These hectares of a once green and pleasant land, have been ravaged by man for centuries to extract these hidden treasures. The valley did not give up its bounty without retribution. It has demanded so many sacrifices of human life, blood, sweat and tears. Most of the landscape now is like a moonscape, desecrated now by large open cast workings and the legacies of old disused mines. There still remained though, the same traditions of mining by a few privately own mines.

Typical of these was owned by the Young Group who own the Great Row and Parklands Collieries to name just two, and are drift mines or foot-rails. Great Row, with access and return that also serve as a down cast and upcast as in a conventional mine with fan assisted ventilation. To give credit to the owners and management, safety seemed paramount unlike some privately owned mines prior to the last great war.

Engine house at top of dip

John Parson operated a stationary electric engine, this small but powerful machine is capable of drawing six loaded tubs each weighing some 15 hundredweights up a gradient of 1 in 3. This dip is about 100 yards long. The sides and roof are supported by rings or semi- circular girders covered by corrugated sheeting. This heading terminates at a junction which once served the Peacock and Spencroft seams, which are now disused. Coal is only drawn from the Great Row seam by another stationary electric engine operated by Steve Trow, who also is the 'taker off' and 'hooker on'.

The gradient down to Great Row is 1 in 1.9 and to the uninitiated is almost perpendicular. To traverse this dip, one had to lower one self down by the roof supports, it is impossible to walk down without doing so. Unless of course like a fly, you can apparently defy gravity.

At the bottom of this dip, two 'stalls' were being worked in the old traditional manner. The two stalls were being progressed opposite to one another, i.e. one to Eastwards the other Westwards.

Joe Swift, a splendid character of good physique, is 'collier', 'loader', and 'waggoner'. This combination of jobs was surprising, for even in the old days working the 'pillar and stall' system, it was normal for a collier to do the coal getting and timbering, plus a loader and a lad to do the waggoning. The only traditional method he did not use, was 'hand holing'. This was done using an electric drill.

"My Grandfaither", said .Joe, *"Before the first world war did the same as ah'm doin' na, except fer me cap lamp an' that electric borin' machine, it anna changed a bit ah tell thee, it's true"*. He paused wiped the sweat from his brow and looked at the roof. *"Just the same, ah lark me Grandfaither but 'e'd got a looder"*, Joe continued. Taking up his large shovel or pan started to load the coal into the tub as though his very life depended on it and, that he had wasted enough time relating about his forebear.

The Fireman, Jack Sharpe, testing for gas with his methanometer nodded in agreement, *"Joe's quite right. Things, except for a few modern appliances like this"*, he said pointing to the gas detector, cap lamp and drill, *"haven't changed since Victorian times. I sometimes close my eyes*

and get pictures in my mind, and noises too of the women and kids, ghosts of the past that have worked in similar situations."
The journey outby was to me to say the least HORRIFIC. The tortuous climb up that dip, was in my mind like scaling the North face of the Matterhorn. Just imagine what it must feel like after a hard days slog of coal getting, being faced with task of getting to the surface. It would surely daunt a young fit athlete. To men like Ken Stevenson and Joe Sharp it's all in a days work.

Tub tipping

Sadly, due to the present political atmosphere when nearly all the Nations deep mine collieries are being closed, these little mines have not escaped the malaise. The result is that about a third of its workforce will soon be out of work and the rest on short time. Soon, it seems inevitable, that unless a drastic change in the so called pundits that govern this once great nation of ours, all that will remain of our mining traditions will be the scars and the ghosts of the past.

Ode To Joe.

Geoff Baker from Kent, was drafted into the mines in 1943, the result of Ernest Bevin the then Minister of Labour who decreed that all men to be conscripted into the armed forces would be subject to a ballot to decide their fate, the mines or the forces. Coal was in short supply, and to increase production, the Government had no alternative but to use this method to gain more manpower. They came from all walks of life the rich and the poor and were called Bevin Boys. Geoff had just left prep school the son of a vicar, and was awaiting call up and hoped he would go into the Marines. Now he and thousands of others were to work in the dirtiest and dangerous industry in the country. He could never forget the conditions and the danger, but most of all the camaraderie of the miners and the warmth of the people of North Staffordshire. He has after all these years dedicated this ode to his dear friend and workmate Big Joe.

I never thought for one moment
That I'd go down the mine for the state.
It was all part of wartime Britain,
When life or death became a question of fate.

It was Bevin who decided in Whitehall
That the coal mines be filled with conscripted.
And although it was not my personal plan
I was one of the first he enlisted.

It came as the shock of a lifetime
to be told that I'd won in a lottery,
A place in the coal mining industry
In a township world famous for pottery.

I arrived on a January evening,
With the rain and the wind all a-blowing.
It seemed like a scene in a nightmare,

And I wondered where next I'd be going.

I found a landlady in Shelton
Had planned to take no less than eight.
I'd already counted up to nine on the bus,
So I sat there and pondered my fate.

Apparently one of the residents
Had a job which engaged him at night.
It seemed quite convenient if I had his bed
Till he returned in the fresh morning light.

After some four weeks or so of hard searching,
And my training for the pit now complete,
I looked for new lodgings in which I might find
Some comforts and put down my feet.

I heard of a house recommended
By a Bevin Boy moving to Brum,
To return to his own native birthplace
And the homeliness provided by mum.

My landlady was, as he had mentioned,
A jewel of a kind seldom found.
And I knew I was there till demob' day,
After each day had been spent underground.

I worked down a mine known as Norton,
Where the miners were wonderfully kind.
They were always concerned for my welfare
And daily enlightened my mind.

I learned a whole range of expressions,

Though the dialect was somewhat confusing
I soon got the hang and the gist of it all.
It was crude, it was rude and amusing.

I suppose one of the things I found irksome
In my new cloistered life down the pit,
Was the question of personal toiletry,
Especially with nowhere to sit.

I sought some advice from my workmates:
"Where's the best place to go in this hovel?"
Their answer was not what I needed:
"Get thee pants down an' goo on thee shovel."

I knew if I walked a mile and a half
To pit bottom, I would find a bucket.
"Thay atna gooin' all that way fer a s***"
Joe said: "Thay't goo 'ere and like it or f*** it."

I found this was quite disconcerting.
There should have been some other way.
Psychologically, I'm sure it was very hurtful,
And constipation's my lot to this day.

I was put with "Big Joe" for my guidance
And a further continuance of training.
But when I went down on the noon shift,
It could have been sunshine or raining.

The night shift seemed totally foreign,
Though I found sleep came easy by day.
I s'pose I was permanently knackered,
And when I slept mattered not anyway.

The humour was always engaging,
And the p*** taking suited my style.
I usually got more than I asked for,
But the work would then cease for a while.

I had many a laugh with the colliers,
Who were always given to fun.
They couldn't have been any kinder
T'was as if I'd been their only son.

The time came to think about leaving,
The war two years over by now.
And I hadn't made plans for my future.
Though I once said: "I might take the vow."

"There's more money in mining than vicaring".
Was the only advice I received.
But the fact that I gave it some credence
Showed that, deep in my heart, I believed.

The advisory council for training
Took quite different view when we met.
I suspect that their judgement was perfect
And I wasn't the first they'd reject.

Of one thing I was totally certain,
That the training I'd done down the mine
Would stand me in good stead for ever,
And the friendships would last for all time.

I'd come straight from school for this lesson,
In what it means to have friends

Who accept you despite all your failings,
And in consequence so make amends.

I have never forgotten the kindness
Of people I'd not met before.
And my life could have been unstinted horror
Without their loyalty, of which I was sure.

G.C.L.Baker.

Snappin' Time.

The conveyor belt carrying a constant flow of coal from Seven's face drew slowly to a halt. The face men, grimy and perspiring from their exertions, listened as the welcome sounds crackled from the Tannoy: *"Snappin' lads. Get your bread"*, intoned the disembodied voice from the control room on the surface. Knowing that Archie, the controller, and owner of the voice, would adhere rigidly to the statutory twenty minutes meal break time, a few of the men hurriedly left the coal face to eat their food in the comparative comfort of the intake level.

"Sit down by 'ere boyo's", called out Taffy, the 'button man'.

Taffy, of course was Welsh and came from the Rhondda, and was in his last year before retirement. He was glad of company to relieve the boredom of his somewhat monotonous duties. He had constructed a reasonable comfortable 'snappin bank' out of planks of wood and 'brattice' cloth. Bob, the face deputy, and one or two electricians and fitters made up the group with the 'Main Gate rippers', and started a conversation about food.

"Wot's got on thee bread ter dee youth?" Asked Frank of his mate.

"Chase an' onion", his mate Joe replied, *"Yer conna bate a nice pace a Cheddar. It's smashin' wi' a bit a crunchy pickle. A pity this inna a pint a Bass ter wash it dine wi'"*. He grinned taking a swig of water from his ex-army water bottle.

"Wot's thar lady gin they ter dee Frank"? He continued as he wiped his mouth with the back of his hand.

"The usual thee knowst, Staffordsher tray bafe. But ah munna grumble 'er knows ah lark jam an' 'ers put me favourite terdee-damson. Ah anna much fer wot ah 'ad yesterdee, thee con keep that apricot, it's too sticky fer ma larkin'".

"Wot abite Jack Smith who werks in pit bottom?" Asked Bill the shearer driver. *"Eh's werked in th' pit na fer nigh on foty year, an' eh's never 'ad ite but black tracle fer is snappin'. Eh must 'ave insides as black as coal wi' eatin' that stuff"*.

"Well, look you 'ere now!" Exclaimed Taffy. *"Black is it? Larva bread is black too, you see, but it is good Welsh food and very tasty.*

100

Lovely so it is with fried bacon and black puddin'. You Staffies don't know what you are missing-And'', he added to emphasise the argument, *"It's a very good laxative you see"*.

Howls of derision rose from the local lads, who greeted this with claims of bacon, cheese and oatcakes, a bowl of mouth watering lobby was infinitely superior to what they scathingly described as processed seaweed.

To any spectator who by chance would be listening with some imagination, would think they were in the large kitchens of the Grand Hotel with connoisseurs of the culinary art, such was the fervent atmosphere.

"Noo me bonny lads'', chimed in Wilf the Geordie. *"Ah will tell yer aboot real food, Aye, ambroosia, food fit fer the Gods. "*

"Amber wots it? '' Interrupted Frank. *"Wot the 'ell is that? ''*

"Why aye man, Leek Puddin's and pease puddin's''.

"They wants Lake puddin's they dust '', retorted Frank.

A low growl from an old collier from Brown Edge opened his contribution to the debate.

"Toke abite good snappin '''. He paused and looked around the assembly. There was a hush as they waited for some words of wisdom from the old timer. *"Yer want ter get some Hurdlebunter soup and Wowlers dine yer. That 'll put some linin' on yer stomachs''*.

Hurdlebunter soup and Wowlers? '' Asked one. *"Hurdlebunter soup and Wowlers? ''* Asked another in astonishment.

They were all agog now waiting to be told of the mystery of these exotic dishes.

"Thase are owd fashioned foods that were 'anded dine ter mey from me owd mother. Nowt better ah tell yer ''.

"Goo on then, tell us wot thee are. '' Said an impatient Bob the deputy, *"Wey anna got o'dee''*.

"Shapes yed soup an' dumplins'', answered the old collier. *Na that's wot ah co good grub ''*.

"Agh!'' Exclaimed Frank, *"Ow yer con eat that ah dunner know''*.

"Yo con o' toke abite food but it's got ter bey grown fost'', remarked

101

Arthur who worked a smallholding when he finished work in the pit. One of the dying breed of miner/farmers. Arthur was a tall gangling figure of a man who was renowned for his practical jokes and whimsical humour. *"That's wot ah'm doin'"*, he added. *"Mey an' Cedric, ma mate from next doer, 'ave planted afe an acre wi' Pentland Javelin taters, an wey're gooin' ter share the crop betwayn us when theer ready"*.

"'ow are you goin' to share 'em"? Asked Taffy innocently.

"There'll be a lot of taters boyo. Will you an' your mate have 'alf each?

"Well it's lark this dust sey Taff", explained Arthur with a surreptitious wink at the other men. *"It's ma land an' wey've shared th' work so wey've agreed that Cedric 'll 'ave every thin' above grind, an 'ah'll everythin' below. That's fair inner it?"*

Taffy pondered on this for a few moments, then protested with some vigour.

"That isn't fair boyo. That means that you will 'ave all the taters and your mate will get all the tops which aren't edible".

"They't raight Taff, ter bey fair ah've promised that next year weyr'e gooin' ter swap rind. Eh'll 'ave everythin' under grind an' it'll bey ma turn ter 'ave th' tops".

Taffy was somewhat mollified by this philanthropic gesture, and asked if they would be growing the same crop as before.

"Oh now", replied Arthur, *"Wey wunner bey growin' taters next year. Wey've decided ter grow cabbages instead"*.

After the laughter had subsided, Harry, well known for his sporting propensities, and a keen angler, extolled the virtues of fish as an excellent source of food. He described in great detail how he had caught a large salmon on a fishing trip he had made to one of the great Scottish rivers. Inevitably enthusiasm took over from reality in describing the size of the fish. As his arms extended wider and wider in the classical manner, the unbelieving groans and pithy comments of his audience grew louder. Harry was never short of a witty comment, due to the criticism, decided to be silent-- for the time being.

Enoch was a South Staffordshire man from Dudley to be precise, and a teller of tall tales of which he excelled. He had listened to all that was said,

102

a little impatient perhaps for he had a tale to tell and time was pressing. *"Ah loikes feesh an o'"* he claimed in a broad Black country accent. *"Yo anna gooin' ter balave thees eether, but it's true as yo is sittin' 'ere. Ah platoon 'ad joost sane off one o' Rommel's panzer divisions in Libya during th' war, an wey wuz a bit 'ungry loike. We wuz down on a beach by the Mediteranean sea, so ah fixes me bayonet on th'end of a pole an went spear feeshin'. Ah doived down ter abite sixty feet an ah coomes across an owd Spanish galleon, that must a sunk abite foer 'undred year agoo. Ah didna 'ave toime ter look rind it much cos ah could only owd me breath fer abite ten minutes yer sey. Any rood, yer knows th' big lantern thee used ter 'ang on th' stern as a navigation laight? Well ah brings that up as a souvenir an' o th' sqaddies gathered rind wen ah lands it on th' beach. Yer anna gooin'ter berlave thees."*

He looked around at the expectant faces, all agog what they will expect Enoch to find.

"Well goo on then wot 'appened? wey anna got o dee!" Exclaimed the deputy.

Enoch had achieved what he had been waiting for. He was on centre stage and played the part to the full.

"Well--", he paused looking around at his audience, *"Ah opened the dooer of th' lantern-- the candle,-- the candle inside was still lit!"*

"Yer bugger!" They all shouted in unison, *"Yer bugger"*.

Small pieces of coal used as missiles were thrown at the laughing teller of tall tales.

"It's true ah tell yer", he pleaded.

Harry, the angler, pursed his lips reflectively and considered this tall tale. Then his face took on a dead pan expression.

"Ah'll tell thee wot Enoch," he said slowly, *"If theyt blow thee candle ite, ah'll throw me fish back!"*

The conveyor started noisily indicating the end of snapping time. Bob, the deputy, gave a despairing look at the laughing faces of the men.

"Crikey", he said rising to his feet, *"Ah've 'eard it o' now. Raight lads lets drow some coal"*.

Loose It.

To those not familiar with mining vocabulary, 'Loose it' means the end of the shift. Except for the odd hiccup occasioned by some minor breakdown, coal continued to flow from 'Seven's' face in an unbroken stream. Conditions on the face were good and out put was exceptional. This was reflected in the grin that lit up Fred Brown's countenance. Fred was the overman and he was elated at the thought of his report he would make to the colliery manager. A report showing the satisfactory state of affairs.

Looking at his watch, and feeling in a generous mood, he gave Taffy a boiled sweet. Fred had a weakness for confectionery, and instead of the usual twist of tobacco he preferred to carry about his person a bag of sweets.

"Get on th' face phone Taff, an' tell them lads that anna werkin' overtarme thee con get off wom nar. It's a bit early but thee've done well ter dee".

In no time at all, and not wanting to be told twice, the men pausing only to take the last drink from their water bottles, and to put on their jackets were on their way out-by. Weary and faced with a mile walk to the 'man-riding' dip, they never the less kept up a lively conversation.

"At gooin' ite ternaight Reg?" Asked bill as they plodded steadily along the main intake level.

"Ah am", replied Reg. *"Ah'm gooin' ter Victoria 'all, thees a amatcher boxin' torment on theer. Starts at eight o' clock"*.

"Torment. Dosna mean tournament?" Enquired one of the other men, aware that Reg's pronunciation of big words left a lot to be desired.

"Same difference", answered Reg with confidence. *"Ah knows wot ah'm tokin' abite. Dunna they fret thee sel youth"*.

By this time they had reached the junction with 'Five's' drift which would eventually lead to where a new face was being developed.

"Owd on, jest stop 'ere an' rade one a thase ite aloud Reg". said Ted, pointing to one of the several notices which had been placed at strategic places around the area. The notices warned of the dire consequences that would occur if the mines Rules and Regulations were broken.

"Wot fer?" Asked Reg petulantly. *"Wey know thase off bey 'eart any road"*.

"Goo on", Ted persisted, *"Just rade that one theer, ah'll bet thee any money they cosna rade it properly"*.

"Dunna toke daft", replied Reg,*"Ah wudna tak thee money off thee. Anybody con rade 'em"*. He leaned forward, shrugged his shoulders in defiance and read out aloud: *"Notice. Riding on this conveyor belt is strictly provided for. By order manager."*

This was greeted by laughter and jeers from the other men and they resumed their walk with Reg protesting that it was his weak eyesight that was the cause of the error that he should have read *"Prohibited"* not *"Provided for"*.

Reaching the return dip they boarded the 'man-rider' trolleys that would haul them up the steep eight hundred metre incline. Most of the men who worked in the seam were already seated and were impatient to be gone. The train guard gave the signal to move. Amid the general hub-hub of conversation, Bernard was asked by two of his mates whether he had been to the last home game played at the local football club.

"Ah did", he replied, *"It wanna a very good game either. The most excitin' thing that 'appened was wen that Yorkshire Terrier ran on th' pitch an thee cudna ketch it"*.

"Yorkshire Terrier"? Queried Stan. *"That wanna a Yoky terrier, it wer an Owd English Shapedog"*.

Stan and his mate were aware of Bernards naive but volatile temperament an had conspired between them earlier to wind him up over the incident. As the 'man-rider' trolleys rattled further up the dip, Stan continued: *"That just shows 'ow much notice they wost takin' Bernard. If thee costna tell difference betwain a Yoky an' Owd English Shape dog. Ah bet thee dosna even know who th' goal scorers' were"*.

Bernard was incensed by this reflection on his powers of observation and inability to identify the difference between two types of dog, and predictably, he erupted into a state of anger. His face contorted with rage and red was plainly visible beneath the grime on his face. His eyes bulged and spitting fury he rounded on his grinning tormentors.

105

"Ahm telling yo' two, it was a Yorky, an' if yer dunna shut up, yo'll get this", he remonstrated adding emphasis with a raised fist.

Most of the seats on the leading trolleys were occupied by the younger men. As soon as the cars came to a halt they dropped off and sprinted the 200 metres to the pit bottom, anxious to get to the surface, the sun, fresh air and freedom, their goal was to be first in the queue. Carl Lewis would have been pushed to keep up with these lads, where fitness had been honed by sheer hard work.

Bob Simpson, the pit bottom deputy, made a futile plea as the oncoming horde streamed towards his outstretched arms.

"Owd it theer lads! It inna tarme yet!" He implored.

He might have tried to stop a herd of elephants for what good it did, leaving him astounded shouting incoherent words in their wake. The older more sedate men walked in an orderly manner taking their place in the queue for the cage. Dick heard his name being called from someone behind him. Fred Cooper was asking him a question, which Dick, being slightly deaf, misconstrued.

"Did Bill Walters get his fliers back?"

Now Dick thought he said **pliers**. The misunderstanding came about because Bill Walters a keen pigeon fancier, had six of his best birds stolen out of his cote on the allotment. He had taken the day off to try and find out who the culprit was. Dick and a chap named George were doing a repair job which necessitated the use of a pair of pliers. They knew that Bill Walters had a pair which he kept in a toolbox on 'Two's' level.

"Ah 'e did". Dick replied *"Thee wer put back the very next dee"*.

"Weer did Bill find em?" Asked a bemused Fred.

"In his tool box on 'Two's level. Weer dost think?" Dick answered.

"On 'Two's level in a tool box!" Fred exclaimed in astonishment. *"Who put 'em in theer then?"*

"Wey, George Smith o'cause. After o' 'e used 'em more than mey".

A look of utter disbelief and bewilderment spread over Fred's face.

"Well ah conna beylave it! A nice youth lark Gudder Smith. Well ah dunna know. It just goos ter show yer conna trust any body ter dee con yer eh? Gudder Smith, well ah'd never thote e'd do ite lark that. Eh's last

bloke ah'd a thote of, it's 'as thee see yer con be wrong abite folk''.
By this time, Dick realised that he and Fred were talking at cross purposes.
"Wot on abite Fred? Gudder Smith an mey borrowed a pair o' pliers from Bill's tool box an' Gudder put 'em back weer 'e 'ad 'em from. Wot's wrong wi' that?''
The penny dropped, and Fred smiled nervously.
"Ah'm tokin' abite them pigeons Bill Walters 'ad pinched from dine 'is allotment. Ah esked they abite FLIERS not PLIERS. If ah were they youth, Ah'd get me lug 'oles cleaned ite''.

In the canteen on the bank, Colin waited for his brother who was late in coming up the pit. Most of the other men had left for home before Cyril and his mate Les came in for a mug of tea and a potato pie.
"Wot dost think abite that youth wey've got doin' th' 'aulage fer us?'' Cyril asked. "Eh's as thick as two short planks. Mey an' Les esked 'im ter let us know th' tarme before 'e left. *Wey wer two 'undred yards up Spencer's dip, no telephone an' wi 'ite a watch, relyin' on 'im ter come an' tell us it wer loose it. Wey thote it wer gettin' late so wey went dine. An'wot dost think eh?'' Eh'd gone an' chalked on a ring tin: CYRIL. LES. THE TIME IS NOW 1.45. The soft sod. Dos eh think wey've got Xray eyes? Weet till ah say 'im in th' mornin'''.*
"Ah well'', said Les. *"Termorrers another dee an' dunner they ferget ter bring a watch. It's nice ter know when it's loose it cos ah dunner lark werkin' o 'er tarme wi 'ite pee ''.*

107

Miners' Grub.

The following recipes were typical miners' food based on a filling diet for four.

Lobby.

1 lb of shin beef or skirt,
½ lb of carrots.
½ lb. of onion.
A small turnip.
2oz. of barley.
2oz. of lintels.
½ lb of peas.
1 small parsnip.
1 lb potatoes
3 Beef stock cubes.
1 Teaspoon of mixed herbs.
Salt and pepper to taste.

Cut the meat into small pieces, place in a large saucepan and boil for at least 1 hour. Add barley, lentils, and stock cubes. Wash and dice the onion and root vegetables, and add these to the saucepan making sure that there is enough liquid to cover the vegetable. Add the mixed herbs, and allow all the ingredients to simmer for at least two hours. When thickening occurs the lobby is ready to serve.

Bread Pudding.

Using stale and left over bread soak bread in milk, or half milk and water, just to cover the bread and leave to stand until soft. Add one or two eggs in milk, according to the size of pudding, add raisins, sultanas, currents or stoned dates and sugar to taste. Stir the mixture to a firm pulp and add a knob of butter or margarine. Empty the mixture into a medium meat tin and bake in a moderate heated oven until a golden brown. When cold slice into squares.

Bread and Butter Pudding.

8 slices of white bread, buttered.

2 tablespoons (30 m/l0 Demerara sugar.
4 oz. (125g) Sultanas.
4 eggs.
1¼ (675 m/l) milk.
Ground nutmeg to taste.
Pre-heat oven 350f-180c, gas mark 4. Grease a 2½ pint, (1.25-1.50l).
oven proof dish. Cut the bread and butter slices in half and arrange,
buttered side up in layers in the dish sprinkling the layers with sugar and
sultanas. Finish with a layer of bread and sugar. Whisk the eggs lightly
and add to the milk then pour over the bread, sprinkle some freshly grated
nutmeg on the top, and bake in the oven for 30-40 minutes until set and
lightly browned.

Leek Pudding.

8 oz. (225g) Self-raising flour.
½ Teaspoon (2.5 m/l) salt.
4 oz. (125g) suet
8 Teaspoons (120 m/l) water.
1¼lb. (550g) Leeks.
Herbs optional. Your choice.
Salt and pepper to taste.
Pre-heat oven 350f, 180c. Gas mark 4.
Mix together the flour salt and suet. Add enough water to produce a light
elastic dough and kneed gently until smooth.
Roll into a rectangle approximately ¼inch (6mm). thick. Chop the leeks
and sprinkle on to the pastry, leaving a margin round the edges. If you
wish, add some herbs and season with salt and pepper. Roll up like a swiss
roll, and seal the ends with your fingers.
Lightly butter a piece of tinfoil and wrap up the roll, not to tightly so to
allow for expansion. Bake in the oven for approximately 1½ hours or until
the pastry is golden and cooked through. This is delicious served with a
vegetable stew.

British Pit Disasters From 1850.

Colliery.	County.	Killed.	Date.	Cause.
Abercarne	Monmouth	268	11/9/1878	Explosion.
Aberfan	Glamorgan	144	21/10/1966	Tip Slide. *
Abram	Lancs	41	19/12/1881	Explosion.
Albion	Glamorgan	278	23/6/1894	Explosion.
Albion	,,	6	10/11/1906	Explosion.
Allerton	BywaterYorks	5	10/3/1930	Explosion.
Altham	Lancs	68	7/11/1883	Explosion
Altofts	Yorks.	20	2/10/1886	Explosion.
Apedale	Staffs	23	23/3/1878	Explosion.
Apedale	,,	9	20/6/1885	Explosion.
Apedale		10	2/4/1881	Explosion.
Ashton Vale	Sonmerset	2	3/5/1892	In rush of water.
Astley Deep	Cheshire	54	14/4/1874	Explosion, Fire
Auchengeich	Lanarkshire	47	18/9/1959	Fire.
Auchinraith	,,	6	30/8/1930	Explosion.
Baddersley	Warwicks	23	1/5/1882	Explosion.
Bamfurlong	Lancs.	1	23/12/1911	Inrush of water.
Bardsley		53	2/2/1858	Explosion.
Barnburgh	Yorks.	4	24/4/1942	Floor upheaval.
Barnburgh		6	26/6/1957	Explosion.
Barnsley Main		13	16/2/1942	Explosion.
Barnsley Main		9	7/5/1947	Explosion.
Barrow		7	15/11/1907	Cage in shaft.
Barwood	Stirling	17	8/3/1878	Explosion.
Bedford	Lancs.	38	13/8/1886	Explosion.
Bedwas	Monmouth	1	10/10/1952	Explosion.
Bedwelty	,,	26	16/6/1865	Explosion.
Bedwelty	,,	23	4/12/1875	Explosion.
Bent Grange	Lancs.	16	10/10/1850	Explosion.
Bent Grange	,,	20	1/7/1853	Explosion.
Bentinck	Notts	10	30/6/1915	Cage in Shaft.
Bentley	Yorks.	45	20/11/1931	Explosion.

Benwell	Northumber.	4	19/3/1907	Explosion.
Bickershaw	Lancs.	19	10/10/1932	Cage in Shaft.
Bickershaw	,,	5	10/10/1959	Explosion.
Bignall Hill	Staffs	17	24/12/1874	Explosion.
Bignall Hill	,,	6	25/11/1911	Explosion.
Bilsthorpe	Notts.	14	1/3/1927	Shaft accident.
Bilsthorpe	,,	9	26/7/1934	Explosion.
Birchenwood	Staffs.	7	18/11/1925	Explosion.
Birley	Yorks	4	23/11/1924	Explosion.
Blackwell	Derby	7	11/11/1895	Explosion.
BlaendareSlope	Monmouth	2	28/2/1901	Explosion.
Blaengwawr	Glamorgan	13	8/3/1861	Explosion.
Blaenhirwaun	Carmarthen	6	6/9/1955	Explosion.
Blantyre	Lanarks	207	22/10/1877	Explosion.
Blantyre	,,	25	2/7/1879	Explosion.
Brancepeth	Durham.	20	13/4/1896	Explosion.
Brereton	Staffs.	3	15/2/1908	Inrush of water.
Brookhouse	Yorks	36injured	4/3/1958	Shaft accident.
Bryncoch	Glamorgan	7	4/8/1896	Explosion.
Bryndu	,,	12	28/5/1858	Explosion.
Brynmally	Denbigh	20	13/3/1889	Outburst of Gas.
Brynn Hall	Lancs.	20	19/8/1870	Explosion.
Bunkers Hill	Staffs	43	30/4/1875	Explosion.
Burngrange	Midlothian	15	10/1/1947	Explosion.
Burradon	Northumber'd	76	2/3/1860	Explosion.
Cadder No.15	Lanark.	22	3/8/1913	Fire.
Cadeby Main	Yorks	88	9/7/1912	Explosion.
Cambrian	Glammorgan	33	10/3/1905	Explosion.
Cambrian	,,	31	17/5/1965	Explosion.
Camerton	Somerset	2	13/11/1893	Explosion.
Car House	Yorks.	8	16/6/1913	Inrush of water.
Caradog	Glamorgan	4	26/6/1906	Inrush of water.
Cardowan	Lanark	11	16/11/1932	Explosion.
Cardowan	,,	3	25/7/1960	Explosion.

111

Cefn Park	Glamorgan	3	----/1964	Explosion.
Cethin	,,	47	18/2/1862	Explosion.
Chanters	Lancs	4	6/3/1957	Explosion.
Charles	Glamorgan	19	23/7/1870	Explosion.
Clifton Hall	Lancs	177	18/6/1885	Explosion.
Coneygre	Staffs.	3	10/2/1865	Inrush of water.
Coombs Wood	Worcester	8	18/3/1929	Fire.
Coppul	Lancs	36	20/5/1852	Explosion.
Cortonwood	Yorks.	4	19/6/1961	Firedamp.
Coxlodge	Northumb'd	26	6/3/1863	Explosion.
Cresswell	Derby.	80	26/9/1950	Fire.
Crigglestone	Yorks.	22	29/7/1941	Explosion.
Cwm	Glamorgan	12	24/5/1856	Explosion.
Cymmer	Glamorgan	114	15/7/1856	Explosion.
Cynheidre	Carmarthen.	6	6/4/1971	Firedamp.
Darran	Glamorgan	27	29/10/1909	Explosion.
Dean Lane	Somerset	10	10/9/1886	Explosion.
Devon	Clackmannan'	6	26/3/1897	Inrush of water.
Diglake	Staffs	77	14/1/1895	Inrush of water.
Dinas	Glamorgan	63	13/1/1879	Explosion.
Dinas Main	" "	7	14/12/1907	Explosion.
Donibristle	Fife	8	26/8/1901	Inrush of peat.
Drumpeller	Lanark	4	28/1/1898	Explosion.
Dudley Wood	Worcester	4	27/7/1903	Inrush of water.
Dumbreck	Stirling	9	30/1/1938	Fire.
Easington	Durham	81	29/5/1951	Explosion.
East Plean	Stirling	12	13/7/1922	Explosion.
Edmunds Main	Yorks	59	8/12/1862	Explosion.
Elba	Glamorgan	11	21/1/1905	Explosion.
Elemore	Durham	28	2/12/1886	Explosion.
Elsecar	Yorks	10	22/12/1852	Explosion.
Eppleton	Durham	9	6/7/1951	Explosion.
Fenton (Glebe)	Staffs.	3	15/6/1963	Explosion.
Ferndale	Glamorgan	178	8/11/1867	Explosion.

Ferndale	``	53	10/6/1869	Explosion.
Foggs	Lancs.	10	7/2/1877	Explosion.
Foggs	``	10	4/10/1907	Shaft accident.
Garswood	``	12	4/5/1866	Explosion.
Garswood	``	14	20/8/1867	Explosion.
Garswood Hall	``	27	12/11/1932	Explosion.
Gartshore	Dumbarton	8	28/7/1923	Explosion.
Genwen	Carmarthen'	6	5/3/1907	Explosion.
GethinCyfarthfaGlamorgan34			20/12/1865	Explosion.
Glyncorrwg	Glamorgan	24**	13/1/1954	Explosion,
Golbourne	Lancs.	17**	7/12/1957	Explosion.*
Grassmoor	Derby.	14	19/11/1933	Explosion.
Great Boys	Lancs.	7	6/3/1877	Explosion.
Great Fenton	Staffs,	8	8/4/1885	Explosion.
Great Western	Glamorgan.58		-/8/1892	Explosion.
Great Western	``	63	11/4/1893	Fire.
Gresford	Denbigh.	265	22/9/1934	Explosion.
Grove	Staffs.	14	1/10/1930	Explosion.
Gwendraeth	Glamorgan	26	10/5/1852	Quicksand.
Hall End	Staffs.	7	6/9/1884	Explosion.
Hamstead	``	25	4/3/1908	Fire.
Hapton Valley	Lancs.	16	22/3/1962	Explosion.
New Hartley	Northumb'	204	16/1/1862	Shaft collapse.
Hartley Bank	Yorks.	4	23/5/1924	Explosion.
Haydock Queen	Lancs.	26	30/12/1868	Explosion.
Haydock Queen	``	59	21/7/1869	Explosion.
Haydock Rock	``	13	16/10/1850	Explosion.
Haydock Wood	``	189	7/6/1878	Explosion.
Hebburn	Northumb'd	22	6/5/1852	Explosion.
Herbertshire	Lanarks.	2	30/6/1893	Explosion.
Hetton	Durham.	22	20/12/1860	Explosion.
Hetton	``	1	6/3/1878	Inrush of water.
Heys	Lancs.	40	31/7/1857	Explosion.
Higham	Yorks	13	15/2/1860	Explosion
Highbridge	Staffs.	3	30/3/1871	Inrush of water.

High Brooks.	Lancs.	30	23/1/1866	Explosion.
High Brooks	"	37	1/4/1869	Explosion.
Hindley Green	"	62	26/11/1868	Explosion
Hindley Green	"	6	/11/1871	Explosion
Holditch	Staffs	30	2/7/1937	Explosion
Home Farm	Lanark	4	23/1/1877	Explosion
Homer Hill	Staffs	12	11/11/1867	Explosion
Horden	Durham	1	23/11/1953	Explosion
Houghton	"	26	12/10/1850	Explosion
Houghton Main	Yorks	7	12/12/1930	Explosion
Hulton Bank	Lancs	344	21/10/1910	Explosion
Hyde	Chesire	23	18/1/1889	Explosion
Ince Hall	"	13	22/12/1851	Explosion.
Ince Hall	"	89	18/2/1854	Explosion.
Ince Hall Harley	"	4	--/2/1850	Explosion.
Ince Hall Harley	"	58	24/3/1853	Explosion.
Ince Hall SawMill	"	15	18/7/1874	Explosion.
Ince Moss	Lancs.	70	6/9/1871	Explosion.
Ingham	Yorks.	12	9/9/1947	Explosion.
Jamage	Staffs		See Bignall Hill.	
Kames	Ayrshire	17	19/11/1957	Explosion.
Killan	Glamorgan	5	27/11/1924	Inrush of water.
Kinneddar	Fife	9	31/5/1895	Fire.
Knockshinnoch	Ayshire	13	7/9/1950	Inrush of peat.
Levant	Cornwall	31	20/10/1919	Shaft accident.
Lewis Merthyr	Glamorgan	2	22/11/1956	Explosion.
Leycett	Staffs	62	21/1/1880	Explosion.
Leycett	"	8	12/1/1871	Explosion.
Leycett	"	8	12/9/1879	Explosion.
Leycett	"	6	16/10/1883	Explosion.
Lindsay	Fife	9	14/12/1957	Explosion.
Llan	Glamorgan	16	6/12/1875	Explosion.
Llanbradach	Glamorgan	8	10/9/1901	Explosion.
Llanerch	Monmouth	176	6/2/1890	Explosion.

Llantrisant	Glamorgan	4	2/6/1941	Explosion.
Llay Main	Denbigh	9	5/12/1924	Explosion.
Llest	Glamorgan	19	18/8/1899	Explosion.
Llwynvi	"	15	26/12/1863	Explosion.
Llwynypia	"	11	25/1/1932	Explosion.
Lofthouse	Yorks.	7	21/3/1973	Inrush of water.
Louisa	Durham	21	22/8/1947	Explosion.
Lovers Lane	Lancs.	27	28/3/1872	Explosion.
Low Hall	"	27	15/11/1869	Explosion.
Lower Duffryn	Glamorgan	19	25/11/1858	Explosion.
Lower Duffryn	"	12	6/11/1860	Explosion.
Lundhill	Yorks	189	19/2/1857	Explosion.
Lyme	Lancs.	5	26/2/1930	Explosion.
Maclaren	Monmouth	14	3/9/1902	Explosion.
MaestegMerthyr	Glamorgan	11	11/1/1872	Explosion.
Malago Vale	Gloucester	10	31/8/1891	Explosion.
Malago Vale	"	2	15/3/1895	Explosion.
Maltby Main	Yorks.	27	28/7/1923	Explosion.
Manvers Main	"	5	4/3/1945	Explosion.
Mardy	Glamorgan	81	3/12/1885	Explosion.
Marine	Monmouth	52	1/3/1927	Explosion.
Markham	Derby.	7	21/1/1937	Explosion.
Markham	"	18	30/7/1973	Shaft accident.
Markham No.1	"	79	10/5/1938	Explosion.
Maryhill	Staffs	3	17/1/1929	Inrush of water.
Mauricewood	Midlothian	63	5/9/1889	Fire.
Maypole	Lancs.	75	18/8/1908	Explosion.
Medomsley	Durham	8	24/2/1923	Shaft accident.
Michael	Fife	9	9/9/1967	Fire.
Micklefield	Yorks.	62	30/4/1896	Explosion.
MiddleDyffryn	Glamorgan	13	-/12/1850	Explosion.
Middle Dyffryn	"	65	10/5/1852	Explosion.
Milfraen	Monmouth	9	10/7/1929	Explosion.
Minnie Pit	See Podmore Hall.			

Montague	Northumber'38	30/3/1925	Inrush of water.
Morfa	Glamorgan 39	17/10/1863	Explosion.
Morfa	`` 30	14/2/1870	Explosion.
Morfa	`` 87	10/3/1890	Explosion.
Morley	Yorks. 34	7/10/1872	Explosion.
Mossfield	Staffs. 66	16/10/1889	Explosion.
Mossfield	`` 11	21/3/1940	Explosion.
Murton	Durham. 13	26/6/1942	Explosion.
National	Glamorgan. 39	18/2/1887	Explosion.
National	Glamorgan 119	11/7/1905	Explosion.
Naval Steam	`` 101	10/12/1880	Explosion.
Naval Steam	`` 11	27/1/1884	Explosion.
Navigation	Gloucester. 4	4/9/1902	Inrush of water.
Newbottle	Durham. 13	3/6/1885	Inrush of water.
Newbottle	`` 13	24/6/1885	Gas outburst.
Newbury	Somerset 11	22/10/1869	Explosion.
Newcraighall	Midlothian 32 **	12/9/1955	Haulage.
Newdigate	Warwick. 4	3/9/1931	Explosion.
Nitshill	Renfrew. 61	15/3/1851	Explosion.
Norley	Lancs. 7	21/12/1868	Explosion.
Norley Hall	`` 12	24/4/1852	Explosion.
NorthGawber	Yorks. 19	12/9/1935	Explosion.
Norton Hill	Somerset 10	9/4/1908	Explosion.
Nunnery	Yorks. 7	3/12/1923	Haulage.
Oaks	`` 361	12/12/1866	Explosion.
Old Coal Pit	Monmouth 11	3/7/1856	Explosion.
Old Park	Worcester 11	26/4/1853	Explosion.
Pagett's Croft	Staffs. 3	30/1/1863	Shaft/rope cut.
Park Slip	Glamorgan 112	26/8/1892	Explosion.
Park House	Derby. 45	7/11/1882	Explosion.
Pelton	Durham. 24	31/10/1866	Explosion.
Pemberton	Lancs. 36	11/10/1877	Explosion.
Pendlebury	`` 6	27/9/1870	Explosion.
Pendleton	`` 8	4/2/1870	Explosion.

Pendleton	"	5	4/11/1925	Floor upheaval.
Pentre	Glamorgan	38	24/2/1871	Explosion.
Pentre	"	4	--/1944	Explosion.
Pen-Y-Craig	"	2	4/12/1875	Inrush of water.
Pochin	Monmouth	14	8/11/1884	Explosion.
Podmore Hall Minnie Staffs		1	16/12/1909	Inrush of water.
Podmore Hall	" "	9	15/1/1915	Explosion.
Podmore Hall	" "	155	12/1/1918	Explosion.
Polmaise	Stirling	3	3/2/1934	Explosion.
Prince of Wales	Yorks.	4	-/-/1918	Shaft accident.
Quarter	Stirling	13	26/4/1895	Explosion.
Rainford	Lancs.	9	8/1/1869	Fire.
Ramrod Hall	Staffs.	11	13/8/1856	Explosion.
Ravens Lodge	Yorks.	6	4/8/1892	Flooding.
Rawmarsh	"	23	20/11/1874	Explosion.
Redding	Stirling	40	25/9/1923	Inrush of water.
Renishaw	Derby	26	10/1/1871	Explosion.
Risca	Monmouth	10	12/3/1853	Explosion.
Risca	"	142	1/12/1860	Explosion.
Risca	"	120	15/7/1880	Explosion.
Risehow	Cumberland	2	26/11/1957	Explosion.
River Level	Glamormorgan	6	9/12/1896	Inrush of water.
Roachburn	Cumberland	3	28/1/1908	Inrush of water.
Rufford	Notts	14	7/2/1913	Shaft accident.
St.Helen	Cumberland	30	19/4/1888	Explosion.
St.Helens	"	6	27/11/1922	Explosion.
St.John's	Yorks	3	26/9/1959	Explosion.
Seafield	Fife	5	10/5/1973	Ext.Fall of roof.
Seaham	Durham	2	24/1/1871	Inrush of water.
Seaham	"	26	25/10/1871	Explosion.
Seaham	"	160	8/9/1880	Explosion.
Senghenydd	Glamorgan	82	24 /5/1901	Explosion.
Senghenydd	"	439	14/10/1913	Explosion.
Shawfield	Lanark	4	4/5/1925	Winding ac'dent.

Shevington	Lancs.	13	1/11/1861	Explosion.
Shut End	Staffs	4	21/4/1923	Inrush of water.
Six Bells	Monmouth	45	28/6/1960	Explosion.
Shaefell(Lead)	I.o.M.	20	10/5/1897	Fire.
Sneyd	Staffs.	57	1/1/1942	Explosion.
South Mostyn	Flint	10	26/9/1861	Explosion.
South Wales	Monmouth.	23	18/12/1876	Explosion.
Springfield	Lancs	2	29/1/1856	Explosion.
Springhill	Ayr.	4	18/7/1917	Explosion.
Stanley	Yorks.	21	4/3//1879	Explosion.
Stanrigg	Lanark.	19	9/7/1918	Inrush of moss.
Stonehill	Lancs.	18	23/1/1877	Explosion.
Sutton	Notts.	5	21/2/1957	Explosion.
Swaithe Main	Yorks	143	16/12/1875	Explosion.
Talk o'th'Hill	Staffs.	91	13/12/1866	Explosion.
Talk o'th'Hill	"	18	18/2/1873	Explosion.
Talk o'th'Hill	"	4	27/5/1901	Explosion.
Tareni	Glamorgan.	2	16/1/1910	Inrush of water.
Thorne	Yorks.	6	15/3/1926	Shaft accident.
Thornhill	Yorks.	139	4/7/1893	Explosion.
Timsbury	Somerset	7	6/2/1895	Explosion.
Tower	Glamorgan	8	12/4/1962	Explosion,
Trimdon Grange	Durham	69	16/2/1882	Explosion.
Troedyhiw	Glamorgan	5	11/4/1877	Inrush of water.
Tudhoe	Durham.	37	18/4/1882	Explosion.
Tyldesley	Lancs.	25	11/12/1858	Explosion.
Tylorstown	Glamorgan.	57	27/1/1896	Explosion.
Tyr Nicholas	Monmouth.	13	27/5/1857	Explosion.
Udston	Lanark.	73	28/5/1887	Explosion.
Unity Brook	Lancs	43	12/3/1878	Explosion.
Urpeth	Durham.	4	17/12/1906	Explosion.
Usworth	"	42	2/3/1885	Explosion.
Usworth	"	13	5/6/1850	Explosion.
Valleyfield	Fife.	33	28/10/1939	Explosion.

Victoria	Cheshire	38	14/6/1866	Explosion.
Victoria	Monmouth	19	2/3/1871	Explosion.
Victoria	Yorks.	9	14/3/1879	Explosion.
Walker	Northumber.	16	22/11/1862	Explosion.
Walton	Yorks	5	22/4/1959	Explosion.
Warren Vale	"	52	20/12/1851	Explosion.
Washington	Durham	35	18/8/1851	Explosion.
Washington	Glebe "	14	20/2/1908	Explosion.
Wath Main	Yorks.	7	24/2/1930	Explosion.
Weetslade	Northumber.	5	1/10/1951	Explosion.
Weigfach	Glamorgan.	18	10/3/1877	Explosion.
Wernbwll	Glamorgan	7	28/11/1928	Explosion.
West Cannock	Staffs.	6	16/11/1933	Explosion.
West Stanley	Durham.	13	19/4/1882	Explosion.
West Stanley	"	168	16/2/1909	Explosion.
Wharncliffe	Yorks	20	18/10/1883	Explosion.
Wharncliffe	"	11	30/5/1914	Explosion.
Wharncliffe	"	58	6/8/1936	Explosion.
Wheeldale	"	9	22/2/1923	Explosion.
Whitehall	Staffs	9	-/7/1851	Explosion.
Whitehaven	Cumberland	4	25/4/1882	Explosion.
Whitehaven	"	39	5/9/1922	Explosion.
Whitehaven	"	27	29/1/1931	Explosion.
Whitehaven	"	136	11/5/1910	Explosion.
Whitehaven	"	5	26/11/1907	Explosion.
Whitehaven	"	12	3/6/1941	Explosion.
Whitehaven	"	104	15/8/1947	Explosion.
Whitfield	Staffs.	24	7/2/1881	Explosion.
Whitwick	Leicester.	35	19/4/1898	Gob fire.
Wingate Grange	Durham.	24	14/10/1906	Explosion.
Winstanley	Lancs.	13	3/8/1860	Explosion.
Woodhorn.	Northumber	13	13/8/1916	Explosion.
Workington	Cumberland	27	28/7/1837	Inrush of water.
Wynnstay	Denbigh	13	9/12/1863	Explosion.

Wynnstay   "   10   30/9/1868   Explosion.
* Although it was not an underground disaster it was attributed to
mining. The spoil tip at Aberfan mostly due to heavy rainfall,
collapsed and slid enveloping the school and killing 116 children
who were at school that day. Several houses were also buried under
45 feet of mud and slurry bringing the death roll to 144.
** Injured.